Walker

THE SCHOLAR-FIGHTER

BOOKS FOR JEWISH CHILDREN BY

LIBBY M. KLAPERMAN

The Dreidel Who Wouldn't Spin
Adam and the First Sabbath
Stories from the Bible
Jeremy and the Torah
Jeremy and Judy say the Sh'ma
Jeremy Learns About God
Jeremy's ABC book
The Scholar-Fighter

The Scholar-Fighter

The story of Saadia Gaon

by

Libby M. Klaperman

drawings by Charles Walker

FARRAR, STRAUS AND CUDAHY
JEWISH PUBLICATION SOCIETY

First Printing, 1961

Library of Congress catalog card number 61–8472
Published simultaneously in Canada by
Ambassador Books, Ltd., Toronto
Manufactured in the United States of America by H. Wolff
Designed by Robin Fox

To my beloved husband, Gil

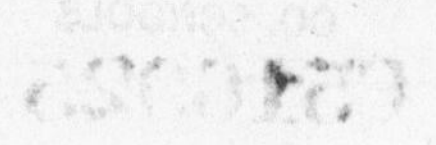

Contents

Author's note

In this book the historic chronology of Saadia's life was followed as closely as possible with two exceptions. For dramatic purposes, the death of Judah, the son of David ben Zakkai, was made to precede that of his father. Actually, Judah died some months after his father. In addition, the ages of both Judah's son and Saadia's son, Dosa, were advanced.

PART ONE

The Flight

1

Run, Run, Run

THE SETTING SUN cast long shadows behind Saadia as he hurried toward the synagogue. Behind him he could hear Mustafa's sandals hitting the cobblestones with a peculiar *whoosh* sound. The sound was comforting in this hour of light and shadow, when familiar trees and bushes took on ominous forms. The walls of baked clay which hid courtyard and shabby houses behind them, seemed formidable and unfriendly. There was not a sound to be heard except the friendly *whoosh* of Mustafa's sandals.

It was the year 915. The two men, the great Rabbi Saadia ben Joseph and his personal servant, Mustafa Ibn Fariah, were in the city of Dilaz in the district of Fayyum in Upper Egypt, where Saadia had been born and had grown up.

Jews had lived in Egypt even before the Temple in Jerusalem had been destroyed by the Romans in the year 70. At that time, the small Palestinian kingdom had been exiled from its land, and its people had been scattered to all parts of the then known world. This was the policy of a conquering nation in those days, to scatter their victims so they could no longer be a united people with a united government.

But although the Jews were scattered in what was called the Diaspora, in different lands of exile, their religion was the one bond that their conquerors could not break. This bond kept them alive from the year 70 until Saadia's day. Fortunately, when the kingdom in Palestine had been destroyed and its schools and leaders wiped out, two great academies had been founded outside of Palestine. These academies existed in the cities of Sura and Pumbedita, which were in Babylonia. At the academies, great scholars, teachers and rabbis studied the Bible and the Talmud. They sent letters called Responsa to Jewish communities all over the world, keeping alive Jewish scholarship and teaching the Jewish people how to observe their religion even though they no longer had a Temple or a homeland. These Responsa actually served as the force which united the Jews in their faith.

The heads of the academies of Sura and Pumbedita were usually the two greatest and most brilliant scholars of that time. Each of these heads was called Gaon, the Great One. Their word was accepted as the highest and final authority.

It was sad that in the tenth century, the century in which Saadia lived, the power of the Gaon had been greatly weakened. The scholars of Sura and Pumbedita were weakening, and as a result, the Jews of the entire world suffered. Since Responsa no longer came from Babylonia with the same authority as before, there was confusion. Some Jewish communities were turning to Palestine, where an academy had been founded in the city of Tiberias, and they were now following the Responsa of Tiberias. This caused friction between Babylonia and Palestine as Jewish centers of learning.

Other Jewish communities floundered hopelessly. In the Near East, many affiliated themselves with an extreme Jewish sect called the Karaites. The Karaites claimed that the Talmud was not divinely inspired. They taught that only the Five Books of Moses, the Torah, were divine. They demanded a strict observance of the Torah, even to refusing medical care, because they said that God alone could heal. The Jews who were becoming Karaites were those who wanted authority in Jewish life. Since the Gaon no longer seemed to give them that authority, they were attracted to Karaism.

Saadia was not yet twenty-five years old at this time. He was tall and thin, with burning black eyes and a handsome, strong chin. He had a brilliant mind, a great knowledge of Torah and of Talmud and an equally great knowledge of science, mathematics and philosophy. His scholarship had won him respect from Jew and non-Jew alike. More and more Jewish communities in

Egypt were bringing their problems to him. They waited to read his Responsa eagerly and spread his fame by word of mouth and by letters. Gradually they began to hope that he would be the great Gaon they

were waiting for, that he would unite them as they had been united when they lived on their own land.

The responsibilities thrust upon Saadia had put early lines under his eyes. These lines did not soften his face. It took on the hard, unwavering character of a fighter.

Saadia was indeed a fighter. He recognized the fact that Jewish unity required someone who would fight for it. Jews were spread wide in the Diaspora, throughout all of western and eastern Europe. If some force did not keep them together, they might, God forbid, disappear. That force, Saadia knew, must be the Jewish religion. He hated the kind of religion which the Karaites wanted—which destroyed Judaism's warmth, its love and its joy. Saadia loved only the kind of religion which the Almighty decreed to Moses and from Moses to all the great rabbis of the Talmud.

As Saadia walked to the synagogue with faithful Mustafa, his mind was busy with ways in which to help keep the Jewish people united. He had called a huge rally for the Fifth Day here in Fayyum. And he was hoping to meet with Jewish representatives from faraway European countries—from Spain and Italy and France. The problem of Jewish unity was a serious one. He would need help from as many people as possible.

Suddenly two dark figures loomed before Saadia. Mustafa came close to Saadia, his hand on his master's back. "I am with you," the hand seemed to say.

"You are blocking my path," Saadia said mildly to the shadowy forms before him. "My servant and I ask that you move from before us."

Although the words sounded pleasant and courteous, Mustafa could feel the muscles in Saadia's back harden as if ready for action. "Besides," Saadia continued, "you are causing me to be late for my evening prayers."

A short, unpleasant laugh was Saadia's answer. "Is that all that worries you? Blocking your path? Evening prayers? You are a dog and an infidel, and you will have no need of paths and prayers where you are going." A knife blade shone in the half-dark. "Saadia, son of Joseph," the voice went on, "you have spoken your last words."

As if all in one movement, Mustafa moved quick as lightning, tripping the man with the knife, and pinning back the arms of the second man. At the same time, Saadia picked up the sharp blade which the fallen ruffian had dropped, and held it as if ready to strike. The man on the ground lay motionless, watching Saadia intently. In the stillness, nothing could be heard but the heavy breathing of the two Arabs. Their white kaffiyehs and their glistening eyes appeared weird to Saadia. Their faces were unknown to him. He had never seen them before.

"Who sent you?" Saadia asked.

"No!" the man whom Mustafa held shouted out. "Tell him nothing."

The blade in Saadia's hand moved ever so slightly and though he did not raise his voice, it carried a strong threat in it. "Who sent you?" he repeated.

The man on the ground wet his lips, his eyes darting about for an avenue of escape. Suddenly his face crumpled. He could no longer be brave, not with a knife over his head. "An unknown man, I swear by Allah. He approached us in the mosque. For five silver coins, he said, see that this man Saadia, son of Joseph, breathes his last. That is all I know. I swear it by Allah, and by Mohammed his son. I plead with you, O great and honorable lord Saadia. You are a prince to your people, the Jews. Be then as a prince to one who is nothing but dirt under your feet. . . . Mercy, O prince. Mercy."

The man whom Mustafa was holding spat eloquently, showing his opinion of his friend's blabberings.

Saadia spoke slowly. "Is the life of a man worth only five silver coins?" he asked wonderingly.

The would-be murderer was puzzled. Why discuss philosophy at a time like this? Now if he were holding the knife—one thrust and it would have been over. He blinked his eyes rapidly.

"My people are starving for bread," he lied. "I would never have been tempted by silver coins. I did it for my sick children. I swear it by Allah."

"He has no children," his companion sneered contemptuously. "He did it for the wine the silver coins would buy. And your life, Saadia ben Joseph, is not worth one silver coin, let alone five. Not here in Egypt."

Mustafa tightened his hold so that the man in his arms let out a cry of pain.

"He speaks the truth," Saadia said wearily. "Do not hurt him. They are both poor devils who know no better. See that your man is unarmed, Mustafa—and then we will let them go."

The man on the ground kissed the hem of Saadia's tunic. "Noble, noble lord. We thank you, kind prince."

But as soon as Mustafa released his hold on his man, the two fled noiselessly, racing down the narrow street, their black cloaks disappearing in the fast-growing darkness.

Mustafa was bent over as if ready to spring at another lurking enemy. "Let us move quickly, master. We must rush to the synagogue, for there may be others lying in wait. This is the second time this week that an attempt has been made on your life. Your enemies are growing desperate."

For answer, he heard the sound of the knife falling from Saadia's fingers and hitting the cobblestones.

"Master, why do you stand there?" Mustafa asked.

But Saadia was already facing east, reciting the evening prayers which he had missed in the synagogue because of the two Arab killers. It never ceased to be a source of wonder to Mustafa how Saadia could control his emotions with an iron discipline. His face was composed and peaceful as he prayed. His thoughts were not on his enemies, but on God's goodness, His greatness and omniscience.

Mustafa stood by patiently while his master repeated the eighteen blessings in honor of the Holy One. All the while, the faithful servant kept his eyes on the street, turning at the slightest sound of even a leaf falling.

"We will go to the synagogue now," Saadia said when he had finished. "Give no reason for our late coming. 'He who guards his tongue and his mouth, guards against disaster.' Let us not share our experience with anyone."

Mustafa looked at his master in amazement. Did he believe that it was possible that these attackers came from among his own people, the Jews? Why else would he ask silence of Mustafa?

Mustafa could not keep his questions to himself. "Surely my master knows that these are men sent by the Caliph's court. My lord has spoken out against the injustices of our government, and the Caliph has been highly incensed. Surely there is no other source of danger to my lord, my master."

"Surely," Saadia repeated in imitation of his servant's manner of speaking. Then, seeing that he had hurt Mustafa's feelings, he stopped and laid a hand gently on the other's shoulder.

"Mustafa, there are many dangers that lurk for me. Some from our Caliph—some from sources that it pains me to acknowledge."

"Is it this sect among the Jews, the sect known as the Karaites?" Mustafa asked anxiously.

Saadia did not answer.

"Then you must leave Egypt," Mustafa urged. "You cannot live on in this fashion, warding off death blows at every turn and every step. Your friends and followers have beseeched you to leave. Why do you stay on?"

"I am not one to run," Saadia replied, resuming once again his walk to the synagogue. "He who starts running never stops."

Mustafa inclined his head in agreement. He had served this man when Saadia was still a child, in the house of Joseph, Saadia's father. Saadia the boy had never run, never feared. Saadia the man could not be different.

Very early in life Saadia ben Joseph had shown his great brilliance. He remembered whole tractates of the Talmud almost as soon as his father Joseph reviewed them with him. Hungry for knowledge of any sort, he would borrow books from the friendly Arab bookseller in Fayyum. One reading would impress a fact upon his mind forever. The bookseller so loved his willing pupil that he stuffed him with everything from books on poetry to books on mathematics. Side by side with his knowledge of Jewish subjects, Saadia absorbed a vast storehouse of information on worldly matters.

By the time he was twenty Saadia had shown his scholarship by publishing his Agron, a Hebrew dictionary which helped fix Hebrew words for the new sciences and subjects of the day. A few years later he had published a paper against the Karaites, exposing the cruelty and needless pain they inflicted upon Jews who followed their philosophy. These letters had established him as a man of principle and integrity, outspoken in his beliefs. Could this outspokenness win him such cruel enemies even among his own people?

Sitting in the synagogue at last, Saadia could not bear the thought. That some of his own people would put a price upon his head! Impossible. How he hoped that the man who had been paid to kill him was sent by the Caliph's court and not by some Jewish antagonists. Over and over again, he repeated to himself, "There are those of my people who would be glad to see the last of me, but never to kill."

Never?

This very week, in two days' time, Saadia was planning the meeting of the entire Jewish community at which time he would denounce the Karaites publicly.

The Karaites were a powerful, fanatic group. As fanatics, they would dare anything, even to kill!

The word burned in his mind. What anguish it caused him to divide his people into "for" and "against" even as he was trying to unite them! How he wished he could escape the intrigue, the planning and the fighting! The dream that was always with him—the dream of Jerusalem, of living in peace in the Holy City—tempted him with the magic it always held. Jerusalem! A longing that was almost physical gripped his legs, caused his stomach to turn and his heart to thump. To live in peace in the Holy City, to study all the length of his days, away from people and problems and fights . . .

He shook his head as if to shake off the dream. To travel, to see Jerusalem was to run, to escape. The Almighty had cast the mantle upon his shoulders. He must remain to fight here in Egypt. And besides—there was the rally on the Fifth Day to consider.

And now the assassin's face appeared before him once again. As he sat bent over a manuscript of the Talmud, his father's teaching came to his mind. "For he who takes life, denies God's very existence. Does it not say that man was created in the image of our God? And he who kills, destroys the image. In effect, he thrusts the knife at God. Therefore—"

Rabbi Abraham Kohen, Saadia's devoted disciple, interrupted him, clearing his throat a few times before Saadia looked up from the manuscript.

"We have been talking—a few of the elders, that is

— Perhaps this meeting on the Fifth Day could be avoided. After all, your writings have made it perfectly clear how you, our beloved leader and revered rabbi, feel about the Karaites. They are really nothing to be alarmed about—a sect of Judaism that is petering out—well, petering away, so to speak. Why make such a fuss about something that—"

Saadia saw his old friend's eyes, and they refused to look into his.

"The meeting is set, Rabbi Abraham. There will be no changes."

Rabbi Abraham's face fell. His lower lip quivered. "It is inviting trouble," he stammered.

" 'Is it you, you troubler of Israel?' " Saadia softly asked, quoting from the Bible.

"I beg your pardon." Rabbi Abraham leaned forward to hear better.

"I was quoting from the portion of the Bible where Ahab and Elijah meet. Ahab called Elijah a troubler of Israel. Though I do not presume to compare myself to the great prophet Elijah," Saadia said softly, his eyes closed, "the trouble is not of my creation, just as in Elijah's day it was not of his creation. True, I have written of my position in regard to the Karaites. But I must bring the message home to our people as strongly as possible. Look how they are weakening our faith, making a cruel and painful duty of religious observance. I watched a boy die the other night simply because his father believed that no doctor should be called. He is a Karaite, indoctrinated with the fact that

God alone is the healer. Yes—God is the healer, but man must help himself as well. The Karaites do not accept this."

Tears glistened in Rabbi Abraham's eyes. "But your life is in danger. Let us pray that the Karaites will disappear. We need you, we need your scholarship and your wisdom. It is not the Jews of Fayyum alone that you serve. It is not only the Jews of Egypt—it is the Jews of all the Diaspora. They look for your writings. They ask for your decisions in law. And now, look what is happening. The Karaites are joining hands with the Caliph. Rumor has it that the Caliph, shocked by your ideas of social equality, has given orders that you are to be killed on sight!"

"No man can escape his destiny."

"Saadia, my rabbi, you yourself have always taught that we should not take a passive role in life. Why stay here, in Egypt, and be killed?"

"I am not passive, my friend. I have a responsibility to fulfill. A responsibility to my people. Look here—is it not so that the Karaites accept only the Five Books of Moses as binding upon them?"

"It is so."

"And they do not accept the legislation of the Rabbis as handed down for generations from the time of Moses?"

"They do not."

"Now what will happen if they refuse, as I hear in some parts of Babylon they already have—if they refuse to accept our holiday of Hanukah because it is not found in the Five Books of Moses? What then? Confusion. Worse still, a lack of observance on the part of our people. Am I to ignore this? I, as a leader in Israel?"

"No, no, Rabbi," Abraham hastened to say. "You can continue with your writings. But not here in Egypt. A ransom has been placed on your head. How can you be concerned with Karaites, with religious dogma, when your own life is at stake? Please, my teacher. Let us cancel the meeting for the Fifth Day."

"I cannot, my friend. The father of the boy who died has promised me he will attend. Perhaps I can save the life of one of his other children. I dare not give up."

"But we need you. You decide matters of law for us. Your name has become known wherever Jews exist. You are important to us. If you were to weigh the good you do against the evil the Karaites do, certainly the good outweighs the evil."

"He who stoops to flattery lowers his own esteem as well," was all that Saadia said. The words were not meant to be unkind. They were meant, rather, to put an end to the conversation. But Rabbi Abraham saw through the ruse.

"I am not a flatterer. I speak what is true. Saadia, you must leave. Your friends beg you. Your people urge you. We fear for your life here. Leave Egypt and live!"

Rabbi Abraham had raised his voice and a number of the elders who had been studying Torah manuscripts came forward. "Rabbi Abraham speaks for us," they said.

His people were right, Saadia thought to himself as

he sat silent before their voices. He was selfishly martyring himself. It was a way of satisfying his own pride. He felt the pressure of a painful headache on his eyes, a pressure that became stronger as the voices around him grew more insistent.

"There is only one Saadia ben Joseph. We must save his strength."

"The philosophy of the Karaites will fall of itself."

"Saadia must be sent out of the country immediately."

"Saadia! Saadia! What do you say?"

It was with great effort that Saadia opened his eyes and faced his friends. "I will know after the meeting on the Fifth Day," he said slowly. "I will make my decision then."

Rabbi Abraham threw up his hands. "But you promise us that after the Fifth Day——"

"He will leave Egypt then," one of the elders said hopefully.

"Yes . . . if they allow him to live," another muttered.

The sad words echoed in the synagogue.

On the very next day, Saadia met with the Jewish leaders of western Europe. The Jew from Italy was a prosperous merchant with protruding teeth, a short beard and an even shorter temper. He had a queer way of speaking Hebrew, adding a vowel, or what sounded like a vowel, to the end of every word. The French Jew had shrewd blue eyes and pale brows which he lifted expressively as he spoke. As for the dark, somber Spanish Jew, Saadia felt most closely allied to him. Perhaps it is because we are both Eastern in spirit, he thought.

Saadia was enthused as he had never been before by the reactions of these three great leaders of important communities. They had traveled many miles to Fayyum particularly to see him, to ask his leadership and guidance. And in what? In the very same things for which Saadia was doing battle. To clear out the Karaites who were dividing the communities in their allegiance to the Gaonim and to the dictums of the great rabbis, and to unite the people in the matter of the calendar.

"You see," Avram ben Lorenzo said in his agitated Italian voice, moving his hands about in quick, flitting motions. "This calendar business can be most troublesome. As we all know, my friends, we Jews fix our dates by the coming of the moon, and not, like other people, by the revolutions of the sun. Thus, the length of each of our months is the time it takes the moon to go around the earth."

"Come, come." Raoul Abrahami's blond eyebrows were lifted in disdain. "Do not give us lessons in calendation."

"Elementary or not, it has to be said so that we know what this whole business is about." Avram flushed hotly.

Saadia smiled at the inflammable Italian, but said nothing. Meanwhile, the Spanish Jew spoke. "I agree with my colleague from Italy. It is always best to start at the beginning. Our month actually is twenty-nine days, twelve hours and forty-four minutes. Now, how do we know the exact start of a new month? Well, in ancient days the new month used to be announced by the Sanhedrin in Jerusalem after two reliable witnesses saw the first light of the moon. The country people and the inhabitants of Babylonia were then informed of the beginning of the month by fire signals. Since we no longer have a Sanhedrin, we now use a fixed calendar as established by the rules of the great Hillel the Second. Hillel was practical and instead of decreeing months by the hours and the minutes, he decreed that some months should have twenty-nine days and other months thirty."

"Which is exactly what I was going to say," Avram ben Lorenzo expostulated.

"And which the great Rabbi Saadia ben Joseph knows without our saying it," Raoul added dryly.

"But I was getting to the point." Avram glared.

Once again the Jew from Spain took over. "Now we come to our problem. Word has reached us, great rabbi, that the Karaites in Palestine have refused to accept the calendar as fixed by our sages. Last year they celebrated Passover at a time different from the rest of the Jewish community. Such confusion there was with the baking of the matzos! Some were baking while others were attending holiday services!"

Saadia's eyes gleamed in anger. "Terrible! Chaos!" he said. "And what did Rabbi Ben Meir, head of the academy of Tiberias, say to all this?"

A veil covered the eyes of the three visitors. They would not speak ill of another rabbi. "He is anxious to re-establish the academy in Palestine to its former heights of glory," Avram answered evasively. "He is too busy, perhaps, looking for means to enlarge the authority of his school."

"And meanwhile," Raoul said with great irony, "there will be Jews fasting on Yom Kippur while others will feast on Hanukah?"

"Never!" Saadia's back was straight. "God forbid it!"

"You can see why we have come here," the Jew from Spain continued. "We have no homeland, no king, no ruler. The one bond between us all is our religion. We cannot let that be eaten into by divided authorities. We need unity. The Gaon in Sura is too weak. Pumbedita has all but fallen. We need a leader whom the people will admire, and who will mince no words in fighting for the right." He looked clearly into Saadia's eyes. "We need you, Saadia."

"We need each other," Saadia responded. "More then ever now, dispersed as we are over the wide, wide earth, we Jews must hold steadfast to our principles. You must strengthen your separate communities to abide by the decisions of our great rabbis. This is our only hope for unity. This matter of the calendar, rest assured, will have my utmost attention."

Saadia deliberately avoided comment on himself as a leader, but Raoul Abrahami would not let the matter drop so easily.

"Pray God that we will yet see a Gaon strong enough to lead and inspire us." He hoped to stir Saadia to some comment, but the rabbi merely responded, "Pray God."

Avram ben Lorenzo cleared his throat. "We are staying for your meeting on the Fifth Day, although someone told us you might possibly leave Egypt before then. Is it true, Rabbi Saadia?"

"I do not plan to leave." Saadia rose, a sign that the audience was over. But his promise to Rabbi Abraham forced him to be truthful. "That is—as of now."

Nothing untoward happened between that meeting and the Fifth Day. It was a clear, sunfilled day. The elders, unknown to Saadia, had been taking turns as his bodyguards. There were always two or three with him almost from sunrise. If Saadia noticed this unusual attendance, he showed no signs of it. Nor did he comment on Mustafa's watchful care at night, nor on the ever-present knife in his servant's waistband.

These extra precautions, however, could not help but be noticed by Sara, Saadia's wife. Walking in the market place with her servant girl Beleta, Sara held her head high, but her veil close about her hid many fears. She usually enjoyed her weekly trips to the market, for she liked the excitement and the bustle of the stalls and shops which lined the narrow streets. Now the donkeys with their loads of fresh vegetables hardly caught her eye. The fears that were in her heart seemed to be all about her, even in the market place. A way was cleared for her wherever she walked, as if a finger were pointing her out as Saadia's wife.

Stopping in the Street of the Potters to buy a vase for the Eating Hall, she chanced to overhear two surly Arabs in a conversation.

"He won't last very long. They have arranged a plot where he will be accused of disloyalty and lack of patriotism. The Caliph is determined to see the last of him."

The second Arab was a short man, more than a head smaller than Sara herself. "You must give him his due. He is a leader of men. He fears nothing but the power of his God, for he speaks out against injustice, though it be to the Caliph himself. Would that we had such a man among us!"

"Since when are you so tolerant?" the older man sneered. "He's an arrogant, insolent Jew. And a troublemaker at that."

The rest of the conversation was lost to Sara. She felt her cheeks flame, although at the same time she was chilled to the bone. The phrases "arranged a plot," "accused of disloyalty" rang in her ears. She was sure they were talking about her beloved Saadia, and she could hardly wait to get home to see him safe and sound with her own two eyes.

Hurriedly she paid the Arab potter for the vase, thrusting it into Beleta's basket, and almost shattering it into a hundred pieces. Her hands were shaking so that she could hardly control them.

"We will go home now," she told Beleta.

"But, Mistress, the vegetables——" Beleta protested.

"That can wait." Sara walked ahead of the girl so that Beleta was forced to run to keep up with her.

"Is something wrong, Mistress?"

"I don't know," Sara answered, her lips trembling. "But it is best that we go home immediately."

By the time she reached the house, Sara's heart was racing wildly from the exertion of her hurried walk. Mustafa was in the courtyard, sharpening a long, thin dagger—an occupation which seemed to Sara to be full of significance now.

"Where is my lord?" Sara asked sharply, a tone she used rarely with any of the servants, certainly not with Mustafa.

"He is preparing his lecture for tonight's meeting," Mustafa answered. "There is no cause for alarm," he added, as though gauging Sara's mood. "He is whole, and well."

Somehow Mustafa's words made Sara believe that her worst fears were realized, that Saadia's life was indeed threatened. "Then danger is imminent," she said. "All that I have heard in the market place must be so. I see that you too are concerned for his welfare."

"I cannot deny it, Mistress. All is not well."

"What then, Mustafa? What are we to do? How are we to save him? You know full well that he has no concern for his own life. He will not try to save himself."

"We must persuade him to leave."

"But how?" Sara paced the courtyard restlessly.

"Mistress——" Mustafa followed her as she walked back and forth. "Our lord must leave Egypt—on that we are all agreed. After tonight's meeting, you and you alone can convince him to go."

"I?" Sara stopped short in her tracks. Her knees were weak. She could not hope to go with Saadia. She would have to remain behind in Egypt. Nevertheless, if this meant his safety—— "I'll talk to him. Yes, I'll convince him. I must. Mustafa, get the camels and the donkeys ready and waiting in the back courtyard of the synagogue. I will pack his manuscripts as soon as he leaves the house. Oh, Mustafa, we must save him! We must!"

Desperately, Sara and Mustafa made their plans.

The courtyard of the synagogue was crowded with men from all walks of life. Poor and rich alike had come to hear the great Saadia ben Joseph deliver one of his famous lectures. They stood about in small groups, fingering their beards and tightening the belts about their tunics. This Saadia was a brave man. He was not only a scholar; he was a fighter.

Tall tapers lit the vast yard. Little boys who had been kept up by their fathers to hear this important lecture darted about playfully, running from group to group until they were caught by their robes. The elders of Fayyum had decided to hold the meeting outdoors because of the press of the crowd, and as the minutes wore on, their decision seemed justified. There had never been so large a multitude in the packed synagogue courtyard.

It wasn't Jews alone who were present. Many Moslems who revered Saadia as a scholar and thinker had turned out as well. Armi, the Moslem mathematician who met frequently with Saadia to discuss theories of mathematics, had brought all his students with him to hear a "genius" speak. Moslem scientists and philosophers stood shoulder to shoulder with Jewish rabbis and scholars. They talked in hushed whispers, waiting for the great man to appear.

"Saadia! Saadia! Saadia ben Joseph!" the crowd began chanting.

Rabbi Abraham raised his hand as a signal to them to master their emotions. "Our teacher is coming out now," he said. His eyes searched over the multitude. "Let not a hair of his head be harmed. I ask you all to be on the alert so that the leader and rabbi with whom the Almighty has blessed us will not in any way be harmed!"

A murmur went through the crowd.

"We are friends," the Arab bookseller who had watched Saadia's career with such great interest shouted out. "And we are soldiers for Rabbi Saadia. Let a hand be raised against him and by Allah, we will cut that hand off!"

"So be it!" the crowd shouted.

Just at that moment, the elders of Fayyum entered the courtyard from the synagogue door. Last to come out was Saadia. As he approached the raised platform, the elders formed a semicircle around him.

Saadia paused for a moment and looked at them. "I will not speak as from a beseiged city," he said clearly. "Let there be no fence between my people and me. I ask you to desist from these unnecessary and dramatic precautions."

Shamefacedly, Rabbi Abraham, whose idea it had

been in the first place, motioned the elders to step aside.

The night was clear and beautiful. A hush fell over the crowd the moment Saadia started his lecture. Even the little boys stopped their darting in and out, their wiggling and squirming, and stood transfixed, listening to the deep voice of the Rabbi.

"I have come to talk to you of a problem that is tearing away at the very heart of our people," Saadia said. "I do not want to talk to you in terms of theology and philosophy. Rather do I want to talk to you in practical terms, about what Judaism means in our real, everyday life."

Impassioned, Saadia went on to speak of the beauties of Judaism. Logically and rationally, he explained that the Lord God of Abraham, Isaac and Jacob did not want their sacrifices and humiliation. He did not demand hardship and privation. He wanted joy in the Torah from them and happiness in God's ways. He explained how the great rabbis, inspired by the Almighty, had made the laws and explanations which applied the Torah to their everyday life.

He spoke for more than two hours, taking every position held by the Karaites, and explaining it away. He never lost his temper or raised his voice. He illustrated his talk with examples from science and philosophy, from world history and experience. The great crowd, fascinated by the amount of knowledge shown by the rabbi, stood as though they were in a magical spell.

When Saadia was finished, there was a silence as moving as the applause of a million people.

"Blessed is the name of Saadia!" the father of the boy who had died that very week shouted out. "Had I understood all this earlier, my child would have been alive today!"

"Hear! Hear!" the crowd echoed. Little groups formed to discuss the brilliance of the talk they had heard. The magic spell of the lecture still was upon them, and they spoke in low tones.

"A genius!" Armi the Moslem told his friends. "This man is a giant among us. Did you see how he weaved in that bit about the Greeks? Although I am not involved in this argument the Jews are having, I can see it all as clearly as my hand before me."

"You are right that he is a genius," a second Moslem answered. "And bear in mind that he is risking his life in order that Judaism may be preserved. He is a man of great principle."

Armi looked about him. "I have heard of his enemies. Saadia would do well to leave Egypt."

Saadia himself had walked down from the platform and was greeting his students and stopping to exchange information with scholars and rabbis. Many kissed the hem of his tunic, bowing low before his great knowledge and wisdom.

Meanwhile, Mustafa, at the outer gate of the courtyard, was all eyes and ears. He had sent a few Arab urchins around the streets to inform him as soon as they saw any wicked-looking strangers approaching the synagogue. One of the urchins now came running breathlessly to him.

"Mustafa—you are right. There are four—no—five —no—countless men waiting in the Street of the Tailors. They are ready to ambush your master, since that is the street he usually takes to go home. They paid no notice to me as I walked among them, and I was thus able to hear their talk. They will kill you as well, Mustafa. I heard them say so." The child's eyes were as round as saucers as he relayed his report.

Mustafa slipped a few coins into the little boy's hand. "Go home now and give this to your mother. You have done well. And do not be alarmed by all that you have heard. It is just the talk of frightened men. Try to forget it all! Pretend that it never was!"

"Will you be killed?" the child asked.

"Not I, and not my master," Mustafa answered firmly. "Now home with you."

Before the crowd in the synagogue court had dispersed, Mustafa had already held consultations with Rabbi Abraham as well as with Sara. For Sara had refused to stay at home. The only woman present in that large gathering, she had been seated at a window of the women's gallery, hardly hearing what her husband said, and watching every movement in the crowd below her.

Terrified as she had been the last few weeks, Sara was calmest of all. Now that Mustafa had told her that the hour for departure had come, that Saadia must flee, Sara was cool. She watched Mustafa as he loaded the camels. The few changes of clothing for Saadia and his many precious manuscripts were strapped to the backs of the donkeys. Sara fingered the papers lovingly. When would she see her husband studying them once again? Would she ever? She fought back her tears.

"Do you think he will go?" she asked Rabbi Abraham as the latter hurried up with two large cheeses. "Will we be able to convince him?"

"He must go," Rabbi Abraham answered. "There is no other way. Now that they are determined to have his life, a man would need a thousand eyes and ears to save him. Mustafa!" Abraham called out. "Do you have my things as well?"

"They are here. All neatly tied," Mustafa answered.

"Then you are going with him!" Sara cried joyously while Rabbi Abraham looked astonished that she could have thought otherwise. "Oh, I am so glad. Remember, Rabbi Abraham, he often grows sad and despondent. You must not let these moods overwhelm him, I plead with you. And see that he eats, for there are times when his meals seem to be least important to him." Her tears were flowing freely now as Sara filled Rabbi Abraham's ears with instructions for guarding the health of her beloved husband.

Rabbi Abraham patted her hands. "I will guard his going in and his coming out. I will be with him day and night. As for food, if I have to feed him myself, I will do so."

Sara smiled tremulously. "Bless you, dear friend," she said.

Mustafa took a quick look around the dim courtyard. "There are only the elders left now," he told them. "My master is all unknowing of what we plan for him. It is time to speak."

The three approached Saadia as he stood sharing a word of Torah with the elders.

"Master!" Mustafa called out.

Saadia's face showed his annoyance at Mustafa as he turned. What had gotten into Mustafa lately, that he even dared to interrupt him in conversation and in study? "What is it?"

"There is evil about, my lord. An ambush awaits you in the Street of the Tailors. A band of ruffians who will not rest until the deed is done."

"Well then," Saadia answered curtly. "There is no problem. We will decide later whether or not to return home or spend the night here in the synagogue."

Sara moved from the shadows, her sudden appearance startling her husband. "It is not so simple as that, my husband. We who love you have been your eyes and your ears. We know that there is no choice but for you to leave Egypt. I have come to implore you. Now that this meeting is over, there are no pressing matters here in Egypt. You must leave. You must. There will be no rest for me until you are in a safe land."

Saadia was bewildered. Sara, his mild Sara, to be here in the courtyard! It was unheard of! Looking into her eyes, which were swimming with tears, he suddenly understood the great anguish which had prompted her to do such an unusual thing. In his heart of hearts he had known that he was shutting his eyes against the inevitable. He could not answer Sara. "What is it that is happening in my household of which I know nothing?" he asked, half to himself.

"We have been planning your departure, my lord," Sara said simply. "It must be tonight. There is no other way."

"We are all ready," Rabbi Abraham said hastily. "The donkeys are packed. Mustafa has a guide waiting who can lead us through the hills to an inn where we can rest for the night. From there—to Palestine!"

"Us? We?"

"I am with you, Rabbi," Rabbi Abraham answered with dignity. "Whither thou goest, I shall go."

Saadia turned from one face to the other. The choice seemed no longer to be his. It was out of his hands.

"We plead with you," the elders joined in. "You have held this important meeting tonight. You have accomplished the goals you set yourself. Now you must be able to continue the fight. You will be of greater service to our people in Palestine."

"Palestine," Saadia repeated after them. The vision of the Holy Land, the land of his forefathers, swam before his eyes.

"You must go," Sara's soft voice urged him. "There is no other way."

Saadia stared at the beloved face of his wife, the familiar lines, the eyes swimming in tears. Yes, there was no other way. "But you will not be able to go with me," he told her wonderingly. "How can we two part?"

"We will yet be together." Sara tried to put confidence in her tones, a confidence she hardly felt herself. "As soon as you have quarters for us to live, Menahem and I will join you. Only promise me that you will delay no longer and will go. If you are to fulfill the Almighty's will, to be the instrument of uniting our people, you must be alive and well. Oh Saadia, my lord, say that you will go. I beg it of you."

Once again Saadia looked about him, at Mustafa and Abraham anxiously waiting his answer, at the elders, trembling at his side, at Sara's earnest face.

"So be it," he finally said with great effort. "So I must run. Run, run, run. It is God's will."

Disregarding the elders who courteously looked aside, Sara embraced him fondly. "We shall soon be together. The days will be as hours, and the hours as minutes. I believe it, my lord."

"And I. And I." Saadia answered. He held Sara at arm's length and looked at her long and lovingly. "I will think of you, beloved, always. Promise me, Sara, that you will write often. And that you will take Menahem to the house of my father, Joseph. See that he studies the Torah regularly."

"He will."

"Above all, guard your own health for my sake, for soon we will be together."

Rabbi Abraham and Mustafa urged him on. There was no time to lose. This very moment, the blackguards who had been hired to kill Saadia might have grown restless, and might be coming to look for him here.

Rabbi Abraham touched Saadia's sleeve. "Hurry! Hurry!"

Mustafa had brought the donkeys around, and now with a hard slap set them moving towards the rear courtyard.

"I shall not look back at you," Saadia said to Sara. "Let us say farewell now. You must stay here. Do not walk with me to the gate. I could not bear it." He lifted her face, and gently kissed her eyes. "Farewell, my beloved."

Mustafa and Abraham half led him away, supporting his back. For a long time, Sara watched them as they walked slowly off. She put out a hand as if to call them, but her voice was powerless. Then she sank to a heap on the stone floor, her body shaking with sobs.

Two of the elders ran forward and lifted her from the ground.

"This is no way," they tried to encourage her. "You have done nobly so far. Do not be faint now. Take heart. Your husband will return."

"Never. He never will return to Egypt. I know it, and you know it as well."

The elders could find no answer. Motionless they stood there, watching Saadia until they could see him no longer and only Sara's pitiful crying filled the silent courtyard.

2

In Exile

"WHERE WOULD WE be without Mustafa?" Rabbi Abraham often asked. Mustafa had remembered to bring the figs and bread, the wine and dried fish on which they subsisted throughout the long trip to the Holy Land. Mustafa made all the necessary arrangements for sleeping quarters, getting straw as if out of air for his master's bed. Mustafa it was who took care of all the tedious details of every problem they met, bartering with the Arabs for fresh donkeys or food, and getting the best guides at the least cost.

Saadia himself spent every available moment poring over a manuscript or writing lectures or comments on the Torah and Gemorrah. Whenever Mustafa decided that it was to their advantage to stop in a city overnight,

Saadia would breathe a sigh of relief. This gave him the opportunity for writing and studying which he wanted to do so badly, and he welcomed a longer stay.

One of his first letters was directed to his pupils and disciples in Fayyum.

"My dear friends, my beloved disciples . . ." His quill paused as a wave of remembrance swept over him. "It is the will of the Almighty," he continued, "that I have left Egypt. May it be His will that I see you again in health and in happiness. My love and affection for you will never wane. I pray that you will all pursue your studies, and that when we next meet again, we will share our thoughts of Torah in peace and tranquility." The letter was sealed. Mustafa arranged for it to go by messenger to Fayyum.

Saadia wrote many letters in those days—letters to Sara and to Joseph, his father; letters answering questions of scholarship which he had taken with him from Egypt; letters developing his arguments against the Karaites; and most of all, letters to the Jewish communities of the world, strengthening them in their Judaism.

Mustafa and Rabbi Abraham Kohen, each in his own way, tried to help Saadia as much as they could. Mustafa kept the clay oil lamp ready and filled, for Saadia often studied and wrote all night. The friend and servant would tempt his master with choice morsels—some cheese and fruit, bread spread liberally with honey, anything to help Saadia keep his body alive and strong.

Rabbi Abraham kept a day by day account of all that occurred, of all the correspondence that came in and went out, of the visitors, and of the events of the day. Saadia's fame was spreading from community to community. Wherever they went, delegations of rabbis and scholars would come out to meet them, honored that a great thinker was in their midst.

But Saadia was impatient to get to Palestine, to the Holy Land. He wanted to feel the earth where the Temple had once stood; to stand on the mountain where Moses had met the Lord; to walk the streets of Jerusalem where King David had danced.

Finally, after many months, the small caravan reached Palestine. Saadia and Rabbi Abraham knelt gratefully to kiss the ground. With eyes closed, and with a joyous heart, Saadia pronounced the Shehecheyanu: "Blessed art Thou, O Lord our God who hast brought us to see this glorious day."

Saadia's heart was overflowing, for his longing for Zion was even greater than that which throbbed in the soul of every Jew—to be in this historic country. But as they became more familiar with the countryside, a strange, depressing feeling overcame Saadia. Everywhere he went, he saw destruction. The Roman General Titus had burned the Temple in Jerusalem in the year 70, and in the almost 900 intervening years Palestine had sunk lower and lower. Streets were covered with stones and rubble. Broken walls dotted the landscape. Scraggly gardens tried valiantly to produce some vegetables for their owners, but it was to no avail.

The cities and villages of Judea were weighted down with poverty, filth and melancholy.

The people reflected the mood of their dwelling places. Jew and Arab alike, they were impoverished beyond belief. Saadia was amazed at the number of beggars who walked the streets—blind, crippled, distorted—they were heartbreaking to see.

In his tent at night, Mustafa could hear the master weeping. It was a side of his character which Mustafa had never seen.

"Master," Mustafa asked one night, when they were on the outskirts of the city of Tiberias. "Why do you weep?"

"I weep, my Mustafa, for the glories of Jerusalem that are no longer."

"But what is broken can be rebuilt," Mustafa said encouragingly. "My master dare not weep for what was. He must look ahead."

Saadia sighed heavily. "So does my own mind tell me. But the heart is hard to still."

The academy where Saadia planned to live was in the north of Palestine, in the city of Tiberias, right on the Sea of Galilee. Tiberias, by daylight, seemed a much more cheerful place than the rest of the country. The beauty of the rolling hills around the city, and the deep blue of the waters, gladdened Saadia's heart. He breathed deeply of the fresh, cool air.

"There is no air like that of the Holy Land," Rabbi Abraham said to him, noticing the upsurge in his spirits. "The air of Palestine does something to one—it is like magic."

The school at Tiberias was in a low, white building whose walls were miraculously intact. In a country where everything was a shambles, it was amazing to see an entire wall. The Almighty had evidently spared the academy the destruction which lay over the rest of Palestine.

"May your coming be in peace, Rabbi Saadia," the scholars at the school greeted him. There were many present with whom Saadia had been in correspondence over difficult points of Jewish law. These men embraced him warmly, grateful that they could see with their own eyes the man whose quill wrote so facilely, and whose mind was so brilliant.

The head of the academy, Rabbi Ben Meir, ushered Saadia and Rabbi Abraham into his private study. Round and rosy, Ben Meir looked as though he rolled rather than walked, through life. He spoke in short phrases.

"Glad you're here . . . help yourself . . . jug of water in corner . . ."

Saadia drank deeply, giving himself the opportunity to observe Ben Meir and his surroundings. He was surprised to see a tall, dark-faced man sitting quietly in a corner, observing him with an intensity that fascinated Saadia.

"Abu Kathir Yahya al-Katib," Rabbi Abraham whispered to Saadia. "That is he."

So that was Abu Kathir, the great Torah scholar! Saadia extended his hand in friendship.

"Two giants meeting . . . good for our people . . . good for the school in Tiberias." Ben Meir beamed on the two men.

Although Abu Kathir was almost twenty years older than Saadia, the two became close friends. Saadia respectfully called the older man "teacher," and they spent most of their days disputing points of law in the Talmudic treatises, developing new ideas and new concepts.

The scholars of Tiberias all studied separately in this fashion. At fixed intervals, they would meet as a body to discuss more difficult passages, and to decide on problems which faced the entire Jewish community. But most of the time they studied alone.

The days began to fall into a certain pattern for Saadia. Mustafa, with his usual knack, had found excellent living quarters for them, a large room, occupying the entire upper floor in the home of a poor widow. There was a narrow outside staircase. Mustafa had hung curtains which divided the room into sections and gave each man a cubicle of privacy. Thus Saadia could light his lamp and study until the cock's crow without disturbing either Rabbi Abraham or Mustafa.

The early hours of daylight were even more precious than the nights of study. As the sun rose, Saadia would put on his clean linens, which Mustafa prepared for him each night. Over them he would slip his tunic, and over that his cloak, which he would tie with a silk sash around his waist. His garments had fringes on them, as the Torah taught, in order to remind him of "the commandments of the Lord and to do them."

When Saadia tied his sandals on, his attire was complete. He would walk the short distance to the school, arriving earlier than any of the other scholars. Saadia felt at home in the large, bare room. The wives of the rabbis who studied at the school kept it spotlessly clean. The benches were scrubbed. The stone walks shone like glass. Though bare of any decorations or hangings, the room had a gracious look. A feeling of godliness and peace entered into Saadia whenever he studied there. Though there was very little to eat, and certainly no luxuries of any kind, Saadia was happy.

In the heat of the afternoon Saadia would return to his quarters, to nap the hour or two which was all that his body seemed to need. Then he was free, to study all night.

Occasionally black moods of sorrow and sadness swept over him. One morning, as he put the phylacteries in the embroidered sack which Sara had worked over for hours, he fingered the cloth lovingly, and a rush of memories overcame him. He thought of Sara and their son. He thought of his father Joseph, and his heart ached.

Joseph had been a pious and learned man who was somehow never able to support his large and ever-growing family. He would rather study the holy writings of the Talmud than earn a living. Joseph had tried everything from learning the trade of the barber to becoming a butcher. Nothing seemed successful. And the more he failed at business, the more Joseph turned to study.

Saadia recalled the humble home of his father; his brothers and sisters seated around the long wooden table; the pinched face of his mother as she carefully doled out the dark bread and cheese.

We were poor, Saadia thought, but my father gave me the richest gift of all, my love of learning. Warm memories engulfed him even now as he thought of the hours of study he had shared with Joseph. How Joseph would lovingly develop a principle of law in the Talmud; how he would show the eager child the different opinions of the great rabbis, and then, finally, how he would tie all the ends together and bring out the final decision.

"Those early years in Egypt," Saadia said to himself, "might have been hungry years, but they were happy ones."

Happy years. Wasn't he happiest when he studied? Saadia remembered when he was still sixteen, how he had devoured all the Arabic writings, profound works of philosophy and questions of the universe. He remembered gratefully his friend the Arab bookseller. Day after day, in the academy at Tiberias, as he answered his voluminous correspondence, as he studied with Abu Kathir, he could think of nothing but his home in Fayyum, the street where he walked, the synagogue where he prayed, Sara, his pupils.

This morning, so many months after his arrival in

Tiberias, Saadia felt the dark eyes of Abu Kathir regarding him steadfastly.

"What is it, my son?" Abu Kathir asked.

Saadia lowered his eyes. So his black mood was already evident to his dearest friend.

"It is nothing, Abu Kathir," Saadia answered, his voice low. "It will pass. These moods of sadness come over me, and I am like a tree that is bent before the wind. I cannot fight."

"What troubles you, *b'nee?*" Abu Kathir asked once again.

"How happy can one be remote from one's birthplace? I long for Egypt, where my disciples were with me each day. I long to see my students once again. I long for my wife Sara, for my family and my friends. Is that not enough to make any man heartsick?"

It was the first time that Saadia had ever unburdened himself to his teacher, and Abu Kathir felt pangs of conscience that he had never realized Saadia's homelessness before. Now he could do little more than touch his friend's shoulder with comforting fingers.

"It is hard," he said. "There is no doubt that it is hard."

Hard as it was for Saadia, it was harder still for Sara. The Jews of Fayyum, feeling the responsibility of supporting and maintaining the family of the scholar whom they revered so much, saw to it that her eating hall was filled and that she and the child were properly clothed. But try as Sara did to keep busy with caring for her aged father-in-law, her son and the household, the days yawned empty before her. Unless there was a letter from Saadia, she remained lifeless and melancholy.

"It is not good for the spirit," Joseph chided her. "I too miss Saadia, my son, but I do not let my longing overwhelm me. Your sad face and weary walk have even left their mark on your son."

Sara looked up in alarm. "How do you mean?"

"He cries for his father almost every day. The servant girl has told me." Sara had not realized that her own melancholy would reflect itself in her son. If anything were to happen to Menahem, she would never forgive herself. Almost wildly, she jumped up and rang the huge gong summoning Beleta. "I forgot my child in my grieving," she said to her father-in-law. "It was wrong of me."

Beleta hurried in, a look of concern on her usually still features. "What is it, my mistress?"

"It is my child, Menahem. I want to see him. What is he doing this very moment, Beleta?"

"He was just robing to come to study with my master Joseph. He brings his manuscript with him. See, here he comes."

Menahem, looking so much like Saadia that Sara could not help but smile, walked gravely in. "Are you angry that I am late for studying with Grandfather?" he asked. "Is that why you rang the bell?"

Sara laughed, a sound which Menahem had not

heard for a long time. "No, I didn't ring the bell because I am angry. I rang it because I am happy."

"Happy? Menahem pondered. "With Father away, can we be happy?"

"Of course we can and we shall," Sara said, catching her father's-in-law eye and shaking her head significantly. "The good Lord wills it that we be separated for a short time. Soon we will be joining Father in Tiberias."

From out of her tunic, Sara pulled Saadia's latest letter, one she had read so often that she almost knew it by heart.

Menahem's face lit up. "Another letter? Is it another letter so soon?"

Sara kissed the straight, small chin, the dark eyes. "It's the same one, beloved. But Grandfather here has given us permission to read it once again before you begin your studying. Am I right, Grandfather?"

Joseph, the dreamer, was already immersed in a Talmud manuscript and gave a sound of assent. "And then," Sara went on gaily, "Beleta will bring us some sweet cakes and wine, and you and I will have a feast."

"Is it a holiday?" the serious Menahem asked.

"Of course not, dear one. It's just a change in your mother. No more tears from now on. Right?"

"No more tears."

"And no more sighs."

"No more sighs."

"We will be happy so that when Father sees us"—

Sara's voice broke but she caught herself in time—"when Father sees us, he will be proud."

A smile broke over Menahem's face. "I'm so glad. It makes me sad to see you cry. I like to see you laugh."

Sara laughed again. Cuddling her son, she settled herself on the pillows and began to read aloud. "Beloved wife, dear son and honored father . . ."

And so the days passed into more weeks and months. Saadia continued studying and writing. His Responsa received a wider and wider audience among the Jewish communities of the world. Besides Abu Kathir, Saadia grew to know Ben Meir very well. Ben Meir was a pious and learned man, a descendant of the famed house of Hillel. Saadia admired him as an excellent scholar of fair and balanced judgment.

Suddenly the peaceful calm of the days in Tiberias was shattered. It happened in a midmorning, when the sun shone clearly and the color of the waters of Lake Kinneret were a blue-green-purple such as Saadia had never seen before. It hardly seemed possible that on a perfect day such as this, a blot should descend on the academy at Tiberias.

It came in the form of a group of ragged, tattered, hungry Arabs. They hung close on the gates of the academy, their silent staring faces pressed against the wooden spikes.

"Leave them to their peace," Saadia said. "They are hungry and ill-tempered, but mean no harm otherwise."

But as the day wore on, and the Arab group around the fence grew larger and larger, Saadia had doubts and misgivings as to their purposes. The stories of massacre and murder which he had heard from old residents of Palestine rose to his mind. What could the group at the gate want?

Ben Meir organized a hasty meeting of the scholars. If there was to be an Arab raid on the small school, then it was best to be prepared. Some of the rabbis were in favor of an offensive—of approaching the enemy and driving them off. But the cooler heads, Abu Kathir among them, prevailed.

"This is nothing but the pressure of poverty," he assured the scholars. "The man whose back is bent and low looks for something on which to vent his anger. We are the closest at hand, and so these poor souls are angry at us. Let us ignore them. Let us go about our business as we are wont to. All this will pass."

The meeting broke up with a general feeling of dissatisfaction. To wait idly for the Arabs to leave seemed impossible. There was too much tension in the air. The Arabs at the gate were beginning to mumble among themselves. All they needed was a virulent leader to set the fire going.

In late afternoon, the rabbis met once again. This time, they decided to approach the Arabs in a peaceful fashion, to see if they could be talked into departing for their homes in peace. Saadia willingly volunteered to join Ben Meir as a delegation of two to talk to them.

The rest of the school watched from a distance as

their two greatest scholars approached the ragged, belligerent group at the gate. The murmurings of the Arabs grew still, when suddenly a stone, hurled by one of their number, whizzed by Saadia's ear. Saadia and Ben Meir stopped.

"Back . . . to the school . . . safety," Ben Meir whispered.

Saadia put a hand on his shoulder. "We go forward, not back." Aloud he called out to the Arabs, "Let words take the place of stones. Stones are the weapons of dull men, and I see that you are men who can think and talk."

Many voices answered at once, some angry and threatening as Saadia and Ben Meir approached the gate. "Let one man among you speak for the rest," Saadia said.

There was a moment's silence, for no one in the group wanted to be pointed out as spokesman. Finally, a tall, thin Arab who looked older than his years, and whose flesh hung loosely on his spare frame, stepped forward.

"It is told throughout the length of Tiberias how your cupboards are stocked with dried fruits and cheeses, meats and fish. We starve in our homes, while you wax fat, hoarding food. Well, we've come to take your supplies. That's what we're here for!"

There was a crescendo of sound from the group around him. "Jewish infidels! Hoarders of food! May Allah curse you all!"

Ben Meir looked helplessly at Saadia. "But what you say is not so," he said aloud. "We have barely enough food to keep body and soul together. We have not tasted meat for many months. We ration our bread, and there are days that we go without. All that you say is nothing but slanderous rumor!"

"You lie!" the tall, thin Arab spat out. "All infidels are liars!"

"Our God forbids us to lie," Ben Meir answered with dignity. "I speak the truth."

"We shall see for ourselves," the self-appointed leader slyly said. "Open the gates, and we will inspect your cupboards to see if what you say is true."

Ben Meir hesitated in answering, and in that moment Saadia stepped forward, his eyes flashing, his temper coloring his face a deep red.

"How dare you!" he said. "What right is it of any man to search the home of his fellow, and to doubt the words of his neighbor! We are as hungry as you are—but we did not storm your doors, or invade your privacy. Does your meanness give you greater rights and privileges to abuse? You would do better casting your nets into the waters of the Kinneret and bringing home fish for your families, rather than attacking the innocent and the hungry! Sow your fields. Reap your grain. Do not find excuses for your poverty by attacking others!

"As for your name-calling, that does not alarm us. We have no issue with the way that you worship or the God that you bow to. No matter how hungry we were, we would not attack you only because there are differences between us. Leave us then to our way of worship, and to our God. You shall not enter this school, for you have no rights here. And if you try, we will meet stick with stick, fist with fist, stone with stone."

Many of the Arabs moved away from the gate, as if turning to go. They recognized the truth of Saadia's words, and the fire in his eyes frightened them. But their leader detained them.

"Yellow-bellied cowards!" he sneered at them. "Do the smooth words of a Jewish infidel hide his deceit and his cunning? Look how he will soon cringe before me! Hear how he will soon change his tune!"

With a quick movement, the Arab pressed against a spike of the gate, breaking it in two. But Saadia was even quicker than he. His hand was on the Arab's wrist at the same time, holding it in a grip of iron. The Arab's fingers tried vainly to lift the latch, which was, of course, on Saadia's side. He used all his strength to press back Saadia's arm, but could not. Saadia held his wrist tight. Slowly Saadia increased the pressure until the Arab cried out. Still Saadia would not let go.

"It is no feat to hurt a man!" Saadia said aloud to the mob. "Your friend can brag, but that is all."

"He does not speak for us," an old Arab called out hastily. "I have been against this idea from the start. Live and let live, I say."

"He is a worthless scoundrel, great rabbi," the others chimed in. "He has never done an honest day's work in his life. He always seeks trouble!"

"You see how eager your friends are to disown you,"

Saadia said to the wretched man whose wrist he held.

"Enough, enough," the man said breathlessly.

"You and your friends are to leave these gates and to return to your homes," Saadia said relentlessly. "I shall hold you this way until every last one of the group leaves."

"Leave, leave," the Arab called out. "He will break my wrist. He has the strength of ten lions. I beg you to leave."

Most of the crowd dispersed quickly, taking the first opportunity for flight. "Who knows what magic powers these rabbis have?" they said. But the more curious and more belligerent remained to see the outcome of the struggle between the two men.

Saadia's voice was calm, although his face was pale and taut. "Know then," he said in a low voice to his captive, "that there is no anger between you and me. Rather is there pity, for are we not brothers, descendants of one father, Abraham? Had you come and asked us to share our slice of bread, we would gladly have done so. But alas, we have no food to give you. We are as hungry as you are."

With these words, Saadia suddenly released his hold on his enemy. The Arab was so taken aback that he stood there rubbing his hand, his mouth open in surprise and disbelief.

"There is no anger between you and me," Saadia repeated softly.

"There is no anger," the Arab said, eyeing the rabbi respectfully, and massaging his numb wrist.

The Arab group walked away, gesticulating and talking of the strange turn of events, and Saadia and Ben Meir returned to the school.

Ben Meir mopped his brow. "I was ready to let them in . . . the cupboards are empty . . . no stores of food anywhere."

"It would have been folly," Saadia answered calmly. "No man can set himself up as master over another, searching his house at will. No man can approach another and take whatever he wills of him. And certainly not because his religion is different, or his customs strange, or his color odd."

"You are right, of course," Ben Meir agreed. After a pause he added, "But I had not the courage to do it."

Not long afterwards, Saadia came into violent disagreement with Ben Meir, a disagreement which eventually led to Saadia's departure from Tiberias.

Ben Meir strongly felt that leadership for all the Jewish communities of the world should come from Palestine, and not from the academies in Babylonia. He wanted to restore the Holy Land to its position of prestige and glory. Because of this, he was ever ready to hand out decisions that were counter to the decisions made by the Gaon of Sura.

Ben Meir now expressed the opinion that the fixed calendar established by the Gaonim should be abrogated. Instead, each month he wanted to announce the day on which the new moon, and consequently the new month, would start—and the Jews would then know on what days to celebrate the holidays which fell in that particular month. In this way, Ben Meir hoped to center Jewish attention on Palestine.

To Saadia, this was a sorry state of affairs. A fixed calendar was orderly. Besides, it had been announced by the Gaonim. Ben Meir's position added confusion, and split authority. This was something which Saadia had fought against all his life.

Saadia immediately approached Ben Meir, for he was not one to harbor grudges or nurse disagreements secretly.

"Have you decided to issue a proclamation, disagreeing with the fixed calendar?" he asked of Ben Meir.

Rabbi Ben Meir shrugged his shoulders. "Nothing definite."

"Are you studying or considering the matter?" Saadia persisted.

"Studying? Considering? I am always studying and considering."

Saadia struggled within himself to control his temper. The head of the school of Tiberias was too great a scholar to be treated disrespectfully. Still, he was anxious to find out exactly what Rabbi Ben Meir had in mind. And it certainly seemed as though Ben Meir was avoiding the issue.

"If you are making plans to issue a decree nullifying the fixed calendar," Saadia said earnestly, "I implore you to weigh all the factors carefully. The calendar has been fixed ever since the days of Hillel the Second. Our people have been living by it, celebrating their holidays at the affixed times. What chaos there would be if alternate dates were suggested to them! Is this chaos worth it? Is this not what we have been fighting the Karaites for? Chaos? Disunion?"

Rabbi Ben Meir heard him out carefully. "There is much truth in what you say. . . . Much truth. . . . But one must read the law carefully. . . . Simply because custom has decreed a thing . . ."

"It is not custom," Saadia exclaimed. "It is rabbinic authority. Are we to set ourselves up as opposing authorities in the minds of our people? Think how disastrous it would be to have someone say, 'I shall celebrate Rosh Hashonna on this day according to the Gaonim of Sura.' And another will say, 'I shall celebrate Rosh Hashonna on this day according to Rabbi Ben Meir of Tiberias.' Is this not an untenable state of affairs?"

"I am well informed on the rules of the calendar," Rabbi Ben Meir answered cuttingly, speaking no longer in phrases, but in sharp, clear sentences. "The four principle rules of calendation have been known for centuries, and I certainly recognize them as binding. I am merely looking into the matter, studying and reviewing the calendar as set by our sages. We have been guided by the time of the appearance of the new moon in Babylonia. Should we not be guided by the time of the appearance of the new moon in Palestine? The difference in time between Palestine and Babylonia is what creates the difference in the calendar. I maintain that the date set for our holidays is inaccurate—of course I am still looking into the matter with an open mind—but over and over again I find that a slight extension of the time——"

Saadia was not ready to enter into a doctrinal discussion at this time. It was enough for him that the rumors were now proven true. Rabbi Ben Meir was obviously studying the matter with a view to issuing a proclamation. He was planning to announce a new method of keeping the calendar.

"I shall oppose you," Saadia said shortly. "I tell you now, Rabbi Ben Meir, I shall oppose you with all the power that is within me. I shall use parchment and quill to fight you as far as I can."

Rabbi Ben Meir rose, his roundness not detracting from the dignity of his movement. It was ironic that Saadia, only twenty-three years old, was gray in the temples and beard, while the older man had his full coloring.

"I do not fear opponents in Torah," Rabbi Ben Meir said. "Your interpretations will be weighed and considered."

"It is not a matter of interpretation," Saadia said desperately. "It is a matter of survival. Our people will survive as a people only if they have one source of tradition. You are presenting them with another."

"Do you think that you are the only one to whom Jewish tradition is hallowed?" Rabbi Ben Meir's voice was hoarse. "Do you think I would dare make a change without reviewing and reviewing again every law and interpretation written down by our sages?"

"You are already committed to the change."

"Nothing of the kind. I am still studying the matter. It will take years for me to reach a decision."

"I implore you——"

There was color in Ben Meir's face as he responded. "In Jewish law, Saadia, you are a master. And though I am much older than you, I can learn from you in matters of philosophy, grammar and poetry. Your name is a byword in the four corners of the Exile. Your Agron and your letters to the Karaites have established you as a scholar of note. But I will not allow you to impugn my motives. I am as concerned with this matter as you are."

Saadia felt limp. If the great sage wanted to come out with a statement against the Gaonic calendar, then there would be nothing that could stop him. At the same time, Saadia realized that he too was committed to his own position. He would have to oppose Rabbi Ben Meir if, God forbid, a change in the calendar was announced.

"Then I can no longer stay here," Saadia said, as if summing up his thoughts.

But Rabbi Ben Meir wrongfully assumed that Saadia was resigning from the school in order to force Ben Meir to agree with him. "It is as it was for you in Egypt," he said hotly. "You preferred to leave rather than to fight a difference of opinion."

Saadia was startled. "That is not so. I had spoken out against the injustices of Islam, and they did not like to hear my voice. You know well that human life means little to the Caliph. Moreover, it was for the sake of my wife——" His voice broke as he remembered that last night in Fayyum.

Rabbi Ben Meir regretted his hasty words. "Let us not part angry then," he pleaded. "You have announced your intentions honestly. I had no right berating you. Stay on with us."

"I cannot," Saadia answered. "Do not ask it of me."

The two strong personalities faced each other. "So be it," Ben Meir finally said. "I ask only that you stay with us until the hot season is over. Perhaps until after Rosh Hashonna."

"You are most kind," Saadia replied stiffly. "I will try my utmost."

"May the Almighty be with you in all that you do," Rabbi Ben Meir blessed him, trying to recapture the old warmth between them. But it was too late. Although Saadia murmured a perfunctory "And with you," Ben Meir recognized that Saadia had already mentally left Tiberias.

The audience was over. Saadia left the study with a heavy heart. He had the feeling that the battle with Ben Meir was just beginning. In a thoughtful mood, he found himself walking near the shores of the Kinneret. For a few moments, he watched a single fisherman as he cast his net into the water, catching a few fish in its meshes. He watched the fisherman as he repeatedly hauled up the net, emptying the helpless fish into the bottom of his boat.

"I cannot escape my destiny," Saadia thought. "I am like those fish in the net. They can do nothing to save themselves, and I can do nothing to change myself. I must be what I am no matter how difficult I find it."

The setting sun was announcing the approach of evening. Saadia turned to hurry back to the school for evening services. Walking through the narrow streets, he felt a heavy sadness within him. The voices of children and parents could be heard from the broken-down houses he passed. They sounded carefree and happy. Why couldn't he be like them? Why must he oppose

Rabbi Ben Meir? Why was the role of the fighter thrust upon him?

As was his wont, Saadia tried to turn all his thoughts on the Almighty, praying to Him for strength and guidance. But what would happen to him now that he was leaving Tiberias? What lay in store for him now? The questions kept humming in his brain.

3

A New Alluf

IN THE LATE autumn of the year 916, Saadia, Abraham Kohen and Mustafa once again set out on their travels, this time turning northward to Syria.

The parting between Saadia and Abu Kathir was a sad one. The great Torah scholar had learned to love the younger man as though he were his own son. Now as Saadia sat before him in his meager and impoverished quarters, Abu Kathir found his heart breaking. He covered his emotions by plying Saadia with sweet cakes which his wife had baked. Abu Kathir's little grandson was sitting on his knee, and the Torah scholar stroked him pensively.

"You see, Hayim," he addressed the small boy,

"Rabbi Saadia is leaving. Leaving the land of Israel. We will not see him for—a long time."

"I pity anyone who leaves the Holy Land," Hayim piped up in his small voice. "I pity Rabbi Saadia."

"You are right, little one," Saadia answered.

There was a long silence in the room while Hayim nestled comfortably on his grandfather's lap.

"It is rare for a man to find a friend whose heart beats as his, and whose mind is attuned to his," Abu Kathir said slowly. "I found it in you, Saadia. It grieves me all the more, then, that we two must part."

Saadia rolled the cake crumbs between his fingers. "And me, dear friend. And me."

Holding Hayim with one hand, Abu Kathir stretched forth his other. "Give me your hand, Saadia *b'nee.* I bless you now that you will bring the Jewish people strength and courage, that you will bring them unity. Though I will never see you again, I tell you now that in your success I too will have success. I shall be with you in all that you do."

"Why do you say you will never see Rabbi Saadia again?" Hayim asked innocently. "Is it because your beard is so white, grandfather?"

A cold fear gripped Saadia's heart. Was he never to be allowed to stay with loved ones? Was he doomed to wander from place to place? And would he truly never see Abu Kathir again?

Yes, his friend's beard was white, very white. The years were flying by rapidly.

Hayim saw the tears in Saadia's eyes and he too

began to cry. "Don't go, Rabbi Saadia. You are paining my grandfather. Stay here and make him happy. Please, Rabbi Saadia. Please."

"Hush, Hayim, hush, little one." Abu Kathir hugged him.

Saadia rose and placed an arm around the older man's shoulders. "God will grant you a long life, and we two shall once again study together."

Abu Kathir shook his head. "No, my son. We see each other for the last time now. Though I wish it were otherwise, my heart tells me it is so. God be with you in all that you do."

Saadia was too overcome to say anything more. He walked from the room quickly, Hayim's plaintive "Why is he going?" still ringing in his ears.

The parting with Rabbi Ben Meir was of quite a different nature. Ben Meir blessed his colleague, but made no mention of the difference of opinion between them. Nevertheless, the barrier was there, hard and insurmountable. For the first time, Saadia could not bear to look in the other man's eyes.

The break in the friendship with Ben Meir made the trip to Syria seem even more difficult than the trip from Egypt to Palestine had been. Saadia could not bear the jiggling of the donkeys, and the inns that they stopped at seemed filthier and noisier than any they had ever lodged in. Though he tried to devote a part of each day to studying, Saadia's limbs were weary, and his head throbbed more often in pain than in contemplation. When they finally arrived in the city of Aleppo, Saadia insisted that they go no further. Jews had settled in Aleppo after fleeing from Palestine in the year 135, at the time the Romans quelled the rebellion of Bar Kochba against them. Although the community was as impoverished as that of Palestine, with families living in simple mud-brick homes, trying to eke out a meager living, their ties with their synagogue and their God were strong. Saadia saw that there was a thriving Jewish community in which he could find peace.

Saadia was accustomed to the beautiful and lavish synagogue of Egypt. Now he noticed with satisfaction that there was great beauty in simplicity as well. The synagogue in Aleppo had a simple wooden Ark which the Jewish carpenters had themselves fashioned. The benches were not covered with rich fabrics as they had been in Egypt. But the worn and colorful rugs scattered on the floor, and some hand-woven tapestries hung on the walls, made the synagogue warm and loving.

It became Saadia's center. He rarely left it except for a few hours' rest each day, rest in the modest quarters which Mustafa had found for them. These consisted of a one-room house, simply and starkly furnished. Besides a table and chairs, it held a chest for pots and dishes. Three large earthenware jugs standing in one corner of the room held wine, oil and water. A small fireplace was the only other furnishing in the room.

Here there was no privacy, as there had been in Tiberias. Mustafa was able to hang only one curtain, since the room was so small. Behind the curtain were the two mattresses for Rabbi Abraham and Saadia. Mustafa himself slept on a mattress on the other side of the curtain. Every morning Mustafa rolled up his mattress and put it in a cupboard which he had built for that purpose. That left the eating quarters more inviting.

With greater determination than ever, Saadia turned to his studies. He wrote Responsa to questions on Jewish law which were forwarded to him by his colleagues in Egypt and in Tiberias. He dictated copious notes to Rabbi Abraham on Jewish philosophy, on questions of faith and science. Some day, Saadia thought, he would combine these notes into one manuscript, answering once and for all the disturbing question of whether greater knowledge undermined faith.

In 921, on Hoshanna Rabba, during the Festival of Sukkoth, when Palestinian Jews assembled on the Mount of Olives in celebration of the holiday, and the time when decisions and changes in the law were proclaimed to the people, Rabbi Ben Meir made his long-dreaded announcement. Henceforth, he said, the dates of the calendar would be different from that declared by the Gaon of Sura. He himself would announce each new month to the people. Rabbi Ben Meir's announcement, on the strength of his great scholarship and piety, was accepted by the majority of the Jews of Palestine.

Saadia, when the news reached him in Aleppo a few months later, was not surprised. That very summer he had written Ben Meir, pleading with him to desist from his planned proclamation. But the letter had never been answered. And now the confusion that he foresaw was really beginning to take place. The Jewish communities in various parts of the world hardly knew what to believe. As the months sped on, and Passover approached, congregations became more and more bewildered. When should they celebrate the holiday? In accordance with Rabbi Ben Meir's wishes? Or in accordance with the calendar of the Gaonim?

Into this rabbinic argument another figure now entered. He was the Exilarch, the head of the Jewish community in Babylonia and the representative of the Jews all over the world in the court of the Caliph. As a descendant of the great King David, the Exilarch was considered the Prince of the Exile. Although he was a politically powerful figure, representing the Jews in political and secular matters, it was not for this that they admired him. They revered and respected him as a leader anointed by God.

In this great crisis that faced Jewish unity, letters went back and forth between the Exilarch, Ben Meir and Saadia. Saadia was disturbed beyond measure. He spent day and night on the problem. He lost weight, his eyes became sunken in and his cheekbones prominent. It was not only the importance of the decision which disturbed him. It was the thought that he was forced to battle Rabbi Ben Meir, an old friend and colleague.

In writing to the Exilarch, Saadia tried not to cast any personal aspersions upon Rabbi Ben Meir. But there was bound to be bitterness. It grieved Saadia, but he knew that this was the role the Almighty had thrust upon him—the role of the fighter. He had not been able to be silent at the injustices of the Caliph. He had not been able to be silent when the Karaites made Judaism such a difficult way of life. He could not be silent now.

"A little rest, Saadia," Rabbi Abraham urged as he brought him a glass of hot milk and honey.

But Saadia, bent over the parchment scrolls, barely heard him. He was writing his pupils in Egypt, a task which he never delegated to Rabbi Abraham, but delighted to perform himself.

"Persist also in this matter, and do not rebel against the commands of God," he wrote. "If you observe the holidays on any different day, then you will be profaning the festivals of God willfully. May it be the will of the Lord that there be no stumbling block and no pitfall in your place or in any other community in Israel. Pray, answer this letter and tell me all your affairs and your well-being. May your peace grow and increase forever!"

Saadia sat bent over the parchement, thinking of Egypt, of Sara, of his son, of his old father. Six years without family, without his beloved disciples. Six years of loneliness, and of wandering. Let's see, Menahem would be seven now. . . .

Rabbi Abraham approached the writing table softly. "Saadia, a messenger from Sura. He has been waiting for an audience with you."

Saadia's head was in his hands, his face covered. "What is it?" he asked in a muffled voice.

"He brings an important letter, he says."

"Let him in then."

The Babylonian Jew who entered was startled to see the great Saadia red-eyed and weeping. He had heard so much about the stern, unbending leader, it was difficult for him to reconcile the idea with this picture of a bent and bowed back. The messenger cleared his throat.

"It is a letter from the great Gaon of Sura," Rabbi Abraham said, unable to keep the excitement from his voice. "It bears his personal seal."

"Read it to me, Abraham, my friend," Saadia said, not moving from his position.

Abraham sighed and took the parchment from the visitor. He scanned it briefly, and his face lit up. "The Exilarch agrees with you! He has written the Gaon to say that your position in this matter is the right one. The Gaon himself—in his very own handwriting. Look, Saadia, look——"

Saadia raised his head. "It is as I knew it would be. The Exilarch wrote me of his position."

"But there is more. There is an assignment!" Rabbi Abraham continued joyfully, knowing that work always helped Saadia in his black moods. "The Gaon of Sura has asked you to issue a Sefer HaZikaron, a Memorial Book, in which Ben Meir's errors in calculation, the proceedings of the Gaonate against him and the reasons for upholding the fixed calendar would be clearly and simply stated. Will you do it?"

"Send the messenger away," Saadia replied.

"But he must have an answer," Rabbi Abraham said, bewildered.

"The answer lies with the fish in the Sea of Galilee," Saadia replied cryptically.

Fish in the Sea of Galilee! Rabbi Abraham wrung his hands, fearing that the endless hours of work had, God forbid, unhinged the mind of his master. The Babylonian Jew had his mouth wide open in a stupor. He could not make head or tail of the proceedings. He looked from Saadia to Rabbi Abraham and back again.

"Master, I beseech you, rouse yourself. What is this talk of fish and sea? Here is a problem of Jewish life that merits your attention. I plead with you. Shake your mind free of these mad thoughts. Think better of the Almighty and His will." Rabbi Abraham himself was almost incoherent, so great was his distress.

Saadia turned his head in annoyance. His eyes were bleak, but his voice, when he spoke, was aroused. "Do not fear, Rabbi Abraham. I merely spoke figuratively. I said I had no choice but to accept the assignment. Just as the fish in the Sea of Galilee have no choice but to accept the fisherman's net."

The Babylonian Jew closed his mouth with a snap. So this was the way great scholars spoke. In allegories!

Rabbi Abraham's brow was wrinkled. "But to accept an assignment is not to die, Saadia. The fish die when they go in the net. How can you compare yourself?"

Saadia waved his hand at him. "Never mind, never mind. We have kept this messenger waiting too long as it is. Bring me a quill and I will write the Gaon myself that his assignment will be filled."

Saadia was determined to finish the book by Elul of

922, in time for it to be read in Jewish communities on the High Holy Days. For the next weeks he closed himself up in his room, writing and rewriting. Although Mustafa came time and time again, bringing fish or lentils or tempting him with some delicacy, Saadia hardly paid attention. He ate very little, just enough to keep body and soul together.

At last the large work was finished. With a sigh of relief Mustafa and Rabbi Abraham watched as the rabbi sent the heavy manuscript off with messengers.

"You will eat now," Mustafa urged the scholar. "Let me cook some fresh fowl for you."

"Yes," Saadia reassured him. "Now I will eat. . . . Now I will eat. . . ."

It had been a long time since Saadia had attended services at the synagogue in Aleppo. The Sefer HaZikaron had kept him busy day and night, and Rabbi Abraham had arranged for a *minyan* of ten men to pray at daily services in Saadia's room. But now that his obligation was finished, Saadia took the first opportunity to visit the synagogue. It was a comfortable Sabbath morning, the weather not too hot, and he was startled to see the small number of congregants praying in the synagogue.

"What has happened?" Saadia asked of a wizened old patriarch next to him. "Where are the Jews of Aleppo this fine Sabbath morning?"

The old man lifted red-rimmed eyes. "They are mourning their dead."

"What do you say?" Saadia asked, shocked. "What do you mean?"

"A great plague has stricken us," his informer answered slowly. "There is dying and loss in every home. An evil disease has swept through Aleppo. It brings fever and stiffness of limbs and choking and finally death." The old man leaned closer. "The Moslems have been hit even harder than we. And they are grumbling that this is a Jews' disease. Who knows but that they may not take it into their heads to fall upon us, and murder us in our beds?"

"Heaven forbid," Saadia answered. But he knew the possibility existed. From his observations and study of history, he had seen how the weakest people, and most often the Jews, were always used as the scapegoat for the world's ills. He stroked his beard pensively.

That very Sabbath afternoon, Saadia insisted that Mustafa lead him from house to house, wherever there was illness, or had been death. In every house, Mustafa heard Saadia ask the same questions. "Where did they get their water? How many families were stricken in the same area?"

Finally, Saadia visited the three wells from which Aleppo obtained its water. He looked into the waters of the well a long time, and then turned to Mustafa.

"Since it is the Sabbath day, we will not draw any water from these now. But I must ask you, my Mustafa, immediately after the Sabbath is over, go to each of these wells. Draw a bucket of water from each. Mark the buckets well, so that I will know from which well each was taken. Then bring them to our quarters."

"I will take the donkeys with me. And some Moslem guards. It is treacherous to walk the streets of Aleppo at night!"

"Treacherous? But it has always been peaceful in Aleppo."

"Not since illness has struck at the inhabitants," Mustafa answered grimly. "Man is set against his fellow man. Each one fears the Angel of Death no more, for they are too familiar with him. But do not concern yourself for me. I am well able to take care of myself."

When Saadia and Mustafa returned home, they found a goodly crowd of friends and neighbors waiting for them.

"What have you been doing, great rabbi?" one old woman called out. "Rumor has it that you are chasing this plague from Aleppo."

"A miracle worker!" the people murmured. "We have a saint in our midst, a man who can work miracles."

Saadia was furious at what he heard. "Stop your nonsense," he called out. "I am no miracle worker, nor am I a saint. I am only trying to find out the source of this illness which is killing off the people of Aleppo. Nor can I assure you now that I will find the source. However, I am using my God-given mind to think. To think this matter out. Now home with you, all of you. Enough of this curious behavior."

But Saadia had not had enough. Before the Sabbath was over, three swarthy, turbaned Moslems on shiny black horses, clattered up to his house, disturbing the peace and rest.

"Is this the home of the man of miracles, the rabbi from Palestine?" they inquired of Mustafa.

"It is the home of a poor rabbi, that is true," Mustafa answered courteously. "But a miracle worker—?"

"Let us see him. We bear a message from the governor of Aleppo."

"But it is his Sabbath. He does no business on the Sabbath," Mustafa tried to shield his master.

"Fool!" One of the Moslems bent down to him. "We

said we came from the governor. Do you think the governor would like to hear that his messengers were turned aside because of some Jew Sabbath?"

Without another word, Mustafa ushered the three into Saadia's room, where the rabbi sat bent over a Gemorrah manuscript. "These men come from the governor of Aleppo," Mustafa hastened to explain. Then, noticing Saadia's questioning look and knit brows, he whispered, "I am sure it is in connection with the plague. They call you 'miracle worker.'"

Saadia's bewilderment turned to amazement. He had done nothing, and already his reputation as a miracle man had spread. Merely by walking through the streets, visiting the sick, observing the wells—they were now looking to him for their cure and salvation. He regarded his Moslem visitors quizzically. "What can I do for you, my friends?"

"The governor of Aleppo greets the great miracle worker. He sends word that if you cure his subjects, the Moslems, as you have cured the hundreds of Jews, he will assure you of the security of the Jewish community. In addition, he will give you fifty gold pieces, and a steed from his private stables."

Saadia was shocked. "But I have not——" Something in Mustafa's eyes caused him to stop. "You must thank the governor in my name," Saadia continued, somewhat haltingly. "Tell him that I will know after sundown tonight whether or not I can help his people."

"Then you will not accept this offer?"

"I need no gifts from the governor. If I can help his

people, I will be glad to do so. Let him, in turn, give my people the same kindness."

Mustafa started to nudge the two visitors, who searched for words to answer this unusual Jew. Not to accept silver or a horse? Mustafa prodded them gently. "After sundown tonight," he told them. "Leave my master now so he can ply his magic arts."

It was lucky for Mustafa that Saadia did not catch the last phrase. Instead, he sighed with relief as the two Arabs bowed themselves out of his room. The sound of their horses' hoofs had not quite disappeared when Mustafa returned to Saadia.

"Master, what has happened? How did all this come about?"

"Rumor. Rumor is more rapid than the plague, and it grows bigger as it passes from mouth to mouth. Rumor has made a miracle worker out of me, and now if I do not produce miracles, in all likelihood, I will be stoned to death."

"Never!" Mustafa was aghast.

Saadia laughed. "Ah, these foolish people. If they had only looked in the well . . . We will wait now for the story the buckets will tell us."

Immediately after three stars had appeared in the sky, a sign that the Sabbath was over, Mustafa and the guards with whom he had made the necessary arrangements set out for the wells. In less than an hour, they were back, bringing with them three buckets of water. They stood respectfully by as Saadia examined the water.

"Aha!" Saadia said. And then, "Aha! Just as I suspected!"

Mustafa and the guards leaned forward. Rabbi Abraham, who had just entered the room, came upon the spectacle of his beloved Saadia peering into buckets of water.

"What is it?" Abraham asked.

"Look here," Saadia said excitedly. "Note the slime at the top of this bucket of water. See the small crawling creatures in it."

Abraham looked closely at the water. "I see the slime, but I do not see the small creatures you speak of."

Saadia put a dipper into the bucket and brought forth some water. "Now, can you see?" he asked.

Abraham was astounded. "They are so small, these wiggling creatures. The eye can hardly see them. I would have removed the slime from the water, to be sure, but I would have drunk the rest. I never would have noticed."

"That is exactly what happened to the people of Aleppo. Jew and Moslem alike—whoever drank of the waters of this third well became ill. These creatures probably carry some disease in them."

"But Master," Mustafa interrupted, "if the people are told not to drink from this third well, it will make life difficult for them. They will have to go clear across the city for a pail of water."

"I made no suggestion," Saadia answered. "I am thinking." He tapped with his fingers on the table. "Assuming I am right, then everyone in Aleppo must do the same thing—no matter which well is the source of their water supply. Let us boil the water, until the time when the fresh rains come to fill our wells once again. Boil it, cool it, and then drink it."

"Boil the water?"

"Certainly. That is bound to kill these creatures off, and to kill any filth they might have left in the well. Yes," Saadia said with growing confidence, "this will rid Aleppo of its plague."

The word spread quickly that none of the waters of Aleppo should be utilized for drinking purposes before it was boiled. In less than two weeks' time, a change was seen in the health of the city. No new cases were reported—and a cheerful spirit reigned in the community. Robberies and deeds of violence were on the decrease once again, and a sense of order and peace prevailed.

The governor of Aleppo, in gratitude for all that he had done, sent Saadia the fifty gold pieces and the horse he had promised. Together with the gifts came a decree bearing the governor's official seal, that the Jews were not to be harmed as long as he was alive. Against Abraham's and Mustafa's more practical advice, Saadia returned the gold pieces and the horse, but kept the scroll. "I have no need of money, nor would I accept it for helping a fellow man. As for the horse—" Saadia shrugged his shoulders. "I shall keep this decree, however. It will be a remembrance of this event."

Saadia, it turned out, would never forget the event. After the plague had left Aleppo, he was disturbed to find he had a new reputation. He was hailed as a "wonder man" and a "miracle worker" and people feared him as though he had special powers. They began to seek him out with their problems. They brought crippled children to his door for him to cure. Childless women fell at his feet asking for a blessing that they might bear children. Gone was the peace and serenity of the early days. Instead there was usually a great crowd about Saadia's door, asking for just one moment alone with the man of miracles. No amount of explaining or scolding on Saadia's part could change their minds. "Did you not rid us of the plague?"

The charm of Aleppo was gone for Saadia. He could not turn to his beloved manuscripts because of the noise of the mob at his window. He could not take a solitary walk, or think a problem through in his mind because of the pleas of the unfortunates. Finally, Saadia could bear Syria no longer.

"The plague that hit the people of Aleppo was sent as a punishment to me," he told Abraham one night. "I had thought surely I would be able to live the rest of my days here, that Sara might soon be able to join me. And now these foolish people have cast a role upon me that I cannot play. Wonders. Miracles. No matter how I explain it——"

"Do not fret," Abraham said soothingly. "It has always been your dream to study at the academy of Sura, to sit with the Gaon himself. Let us go to Sura then."

Saadia was tempted, but the Gaon of Sura had never officially invited him to come. He knew it was false pride which held him back, but he could not go to Sura. Not without the special invitation.

"Bagdad, then," Rabbi Abraham offered helpfully. "Did you not exchange letters with David ben Zakkai, the Exilarch? He lives in Bagdad. He would be most happy to see you. And there is a wonderful Jewish community in Bagdad. I hear there are scholars and teachers beyond compare. You could continue in your studies——"

"The Caliph too lives in Bagdad," Saadia interrupted dryly.

"And if he does?"

"Have you forgotten so soon? In Fayyum, there was a price on my head."

Rabbi Abraham was thoughtful. Bagdad would actually be the best place for Saadia to be. After all, David ben Zakkai, the Exilarch, was the most important Jew in the political world. He could do a great deal for Saadia, Abraham thought to himself. A word from David ben Zakkai and there was no doubt that Saadia would be invited to Sura. After all, it was the Exilarch who appointed the Gaon. Yes, Abraham thought. Bagdad was the place to go. He had ambitions for Saadia that the latter hardly knew of.

"I have it!" Rabbi Abraham's eyes sparkled. "We will write to the Exilarch himself, and explain the entire matter. We will say that we plan to visit Bagdad, and would the Caliph represent a threat to our safety. We will write it most diplomatically."

"Not we. You," Saadia answered. "I will go anywhere, just to be rid of these foolish, miracle-seeking people."

Abraham sighed in relief. "We will go to Bagdad," he said softly.

Bagdad! Saadia and Rabbi Abraham were more than a little bewildered by the noise and confusion of the great city, the city which had been especially built to serve as the capital for the Caliph. It was a gay and lively place. Richly clothed Arabs, fierce soldiers and bedraggled Bedouins filled the crowded, narrow streets. The women dressed in black, with bangles hanging from their foreheads and rings in their ears and noses, moved noiselessly among the crowd. Little stalls displayed tempting wares to the passersby, and beaded curtains disguised entrances which looked as though they hid great secrets. Above the low buildings could be seen the great domed mosques where the Arabs worshiped. The slender minarets pointed into the skies, and Saadia was amazed at the beauty and symmetry of their structure.

The synagogues of Bagdad were as sumptuous as the rest of the city. Their richly carved woods and plush benches made a deep contrast to the simplicity of the synagogue in Aleppo. Rabbi Abraham vowed many times that he had never seen anything so beautiful in his life.

Happiest of all was Mustafa, for he had his own family and friends in Bagdad, and a steady stream of them came visiting, bringing gifts and dainties. To see

Mustafa treated with such respect and admiration was a source of great pleasure to Saadia.

"I see that your kinsmen revere you," he told Mustafa. "Blessed is the man who has the respect of his family."

The loyal servant smiled broadly. "I have great standing among them because of you, Master. They know that I serve a great and renowned scholar."

"And miracle worker," Abraham added with a twinkle in his eye.

Saadia laughed. "Let us hear no more of that unhappy episode."

Mustafa's relatives helped him find a magnificent dwelling place for Saadia. Abraham called it a veritable palace. The dark wood furniture glowed with a high polish. Thick carpets covered the floors. Elaborate tapestries hung on the walls. Abraham admired most of all a hanging candelabrum, made of iron, which burned oil. It was a fascinating piece, and at night it lit the room in softly glowing light.

The Jews of Bagdad paid homage to the great scholar who was in their midst, welcoming him officially on his very first Sabbath in the synagogue.

"We have heard," their spokesman said, "that the great Saadia plans to spend but a short time here with us. It is our hope that he will learn to love Bagdad, and will settle here, and serve as our rabbi."

"It was a great compliment to you," Rabbi Abraham, most pleased, told Saadia later. "Many rabbis have passed through Bagdad but none were asked to stay on."

Saadia waved the thought aside. He did not like flattery of any kind, nor did he ever dwell on the praise men lavished upon him.

"But the Exilarch has not even acknowledged my presence," he said to Abraham, in an effort to deflate him. "After all the correspondence you had with him, and the warm assurances that the Caliph was once again my friend, he acts as though he hardly knows of our arrival."

"He will come. He will come," Rabbi Abraham answered.

The very next day David ben Zakkai came officially to welcome Saadia. As a descendant of the great King David, the Prince of the Exile had an appearance as of royalty. Slaves carried him to Saadia's house in an elaborate gilded chair which was set with rubies and diamonds. The Exilarch himself was dressed in the purple silk robes of his office, his turban sparkling with jewels. People lined the streets watching his approach, and bowing before him as before a king.

David ben Zakkai was a massive man, with a large head and thick neck. He was more than six feet tall, with an erect bearing and a strong, firm gait. Saadia was impressed by his self-assurance, by the positive way in which he did everything.

For his part, David ben Zakkai could hardly believe that the Egyptian scholar was barely thirty years old. Saadia's face was already worn. His beard had as many white hairs in it as black. Nevertheless, his thin figure implied a hidden strength which the Exilarch found interesting.

"It is a distinct honor for me to meet you," David ben Zakkai said now. "Our correspondence gave me quite a different picture of you."

Saadia lifted his eyebrow. "So?"

"I thought of a small man—that is—I never imagined you——" For the first time in his life David ben Zakkai was ill at ease before the steady open gaze of the rabbi. Rapidly he changed the subject. "The Caliph has forgiven you, officially that is. Unofficially, he may still resent the frank remarks you made in Egypt."

If David ben Zakkai thought to put Saadia to discomfort, he was disappointed. Although Rabbi Abraham, standing behind Saadia's chair, could not help but give an exclamation of dismay, Saadia sat unperturbed.

"I cannot see how a powerful potentate can be disturbed by the criticism of a single human being," Saadia said.

David ben Zakkai laughed noisily. To himself he thought, this man might be a powerful opponent. Aloud he said, "I admire your courage, Rabbi Saadia. The Caliph bears no grudge against you. He and I have had many long talks about you, and we have watched your career together."

Rabbi Abraham took this as a good omen. Career! Something special for his rabbi! He felt his cheeks tingle with pride.

But Saadia was cool. "I am grateful to you, David ben Zakkai," he said, "for all the kindness you have done me."

What Rabbi Abraham did not sense was the barrier that immediately existed between the two men. Perhaps it was because they were both so strong-willed, so determined and committed to what they believed. Perhaps it was just David ben Zakkai's overconfidence, the way he waved his jeweled hands when he spoke, the authoritative way in which he said even the simplist thing. Yes, the barrier was there.

The two men sat together and discussed problems which faced Jewry all over the world. The Exilarch touched briefly on Saadia's Sefer HaZikaron, emphasizing his admiration for the work as a great literary achievement. Saadia, however, would not allow him to dwell on it. It had been the source of Ben Meir's vanquishment and he could not bear to think of it.

"Revered rabbi," David ben Zakkai continued, "I have come here on a twofold mission. First and foremost, to bid you welcome to Babylonia. The second part of my mission is actually a request."

"You need but ask and it is yours," Saadia answered politely.

"It is a request that I make on behalf of the masters of the academy of Sura."

At these words, Saadia's heart began to beat violently. He could not believe that the fondest wishes of his heart were being fulfilled, that he would be in a position to study and learn at the academy of Sura. The thought flashed across his mind that David ben Zakkai could have written this to him in Aleppo. Why did he wait until he arrived in Bagdad?

But David ben Zakkai hardly noticed the turmoil in the young scholar's heart. "I know you have but recently arrived in Bagdad, and it seems hardly right for you to have to move once again. But it would be our great privilege if you would consent to be a member of our academy in Sura. You could start your new duties as of Elul of the coming year immediately after the summer. This will give you a few months here in Bagdad, as well as time enough to travel to Sura."

Saadia was too overcome to answer. He whispered a prayer of thanksgiving to the Almighty for having brought him this great honor. At the same time, in the back of his mind, he tried to understand why David ben Zakkai hadn't written this to him in Aleppo. He would surely have gone directly to Sura from there.

The Exilarch mistook Saadia's stillness for hesitation. "We need men like you, Saadia ben Joseph. Men who are fearless, who will make rapid decisions and who will not vacillate. You have shown yourself to be an outspoken fighter, a scholar who is not only a man of the book but a leader of his people. The academy at Sura needs your strength, your courage, your guidance."

"The Almighty has seen fit to reward you for all your labor in His vineyard," Rabbi Abraham exclaimed joyfully. "Surely you will not deny this opportunity to serve Him further."

"You can bring your family to Sura. Living quarters will be provided for you, so that you can judge our people with a tranquil mind."

Saadia had started at the Exilarch's last words. "Bring your family" rang in his ears. To have his beloved wife near him, to hold his son once again, to see his aged father with his own eyes! Tears blurred his vision.

David ben Zakkai felt warmth for this strong man who was not ashamed to cry. "Then you will accept?" he asked gently.

"It is a great honor for me to do so. Tears flow from my eyes in happiness that I have been chosen by the Lord to serve Him in Sura."

Rabbi Abraham hurried to bring out a fresh jug of wine, and poured goblets for David ben Zakkai, Saadia and himself.

"To Saadia ben Joseph," the Exilarch said. "May he bring added glory to our people in his new position as Alluf at Sura. May the Lord grant him good health, great vision and a long life."

"Amen" Rabbi Abraham said, pronouncing the blessing over wine and drinking heartily. "Amen."

When their royal visitor had left them, Saadia sat pensively at his writing table.

"Rejoice," Abraham encouraged him. "This is the day the Lord has made. Let us rejoice and be glad in it."

"I rejoice," Saadia answered, "but I cannot help but think of the Exilarch. He knew of this appointment to

Sura, yet waited until we arrived here to tell us. He is a man who likes to pull the strings. Such a man, no matter how goodhearted he may be, is always a danger."

"You will probably never have to do with him again," Abraham answered. "There is naught between you and him but a packet of letters. Why dwell on it?"

"Even so. Even so."

"But you've forgotten the most important thing," Rabbi Abraham said, turning to a new subject. "You can send for your family now."

The words had their desired effect. Saadia left all thoughts of David ben Zakkai and his personality. He called for parchment and quill and immediately sat down to write to Sara in Egypt.

"My dear wife, beloved son and honored father. I pray the Almighty that this letter finds you in good health. As for me, I am now in Babylonia where I have been blessed with God's great goodness. I have been invited to become Alluf, a member of the academy of Sura, and if it is the Lord's good will, I will sit with the great scholars of our time. I write you now and urge you to pack our belongings and join me in Sura. I pray that my father Joseph will not find the trip too hard, and that my eyes will soon behold you all again. It has been seven long years since last we saw each other. . . ."

Seven long years. Saadia allowed the tears to flow from his eyes. He had been alone for so long. Now at last he would have his loved ones near. He would be able to study with his own son. And he would have

Joseph nearby. And Sara. The dear faces rose before his eyes, and he could not control his great longing.

"Beloved wife and father," he continued writing. "Make haste, I pray you. My heart longs for you, longs yearningly."

He signed his name to the letter, and was about to roll the parchment up and dispatch it, when he remembered something. A smile hovered about his lips as he slowly spelled another word out. Joseph would be pleased at the signature. And Sara would be proud. Yes, it meant much to them. This would be the first time he had used it, but from now on it would have to be a part of his signature on all official documents.

In large, clear letters, Saadia had written, "Saadia ben Joseph, Alluf of Sura."

PART TWO

The Flight Continues

4

A Blind Man's Warning

SAADIA had decided to leave Bagdad before the Shevuoth holiday so that he would have time to settle in Sura before the heat of the summer. He was hoping, too, that Sara would be there by that time. Since living quarters were assured him there was no longer the urgency to rush on ahead in order to find a place to live. This gave him almost three months to spend in Bagdad.

In these three months, in spite of Saadia's awareness of Ben Zakkai's dictatorial nature, a bond of mutual respect grew up between the two men. Ben Zakkai liked to feel power in his hands. He often boasted to Saadia, "I can make men and I can break them." While this was true, Saadia also recognized David ben Zakkai to be a man of principle and dedicated devotion.

Time and again, Saadia watched the Exilarch adroitly manipulate political circumstance so that they would bring greater improvements in the lot of his people. David ben Zakkai was not afraid to speak up to the Caliph himself, although a lesser man might very well have been silenced by the power of life and death that the Caliph wielded. Wherever and whenever he felt he was right, the Exilarch showed a fearless courage and an intrepid spirit that made Saadia admire him.

During these months too, while Saadia's longing for Sara, his son and his beloved father were greater than ever, he found solace and comfort in the house of David ben Zakkai. The Exilarch's son, Judah, completely captured his heart. Judah was a young man, just beginning to grow a beard. His mind was quick and keen, and his personality was warm and friendly. Saadia spent a great deal of time with the lad, giving him all the pent-up love and affection which he normally would have given to his own son.

"In my heart and mind," Saadia often said to Judah, "you will always be *b'nee,* my son."

The youth returned the love and the admiration of the teacher a thousandfold. Their long walks and hours of study together opened Judah's mind to the beauties and intricacies of the sciences as well as to the great truths of Jewish law and philosophy.

There was one man in the Jewish community of Bagdad, a close friend of David ben Zakkai's, whom Saadia could not tolerate. Aaron ben Joseph ibn Sarjadah was a wealthy merchant who was considered learned in Jewish law and held a reputation as a scholar of sorts. He gave great sums of money for charity, and was active in many causes on behalf of the Jewish people. With all these great qualifications, he should have been admired and respected. However, this was not the case. There was a grasping meanness in the man which Saadia recognized immediately. More important, there was a basic deceit, for Ibn Sarjadah performed all these good deeds only for the sake of the rewards or honors they brought him.

One Sabbath afternoon, when Saadia had finished studying with Judah, he walked into Ben Zakkai's room to find him closeted with Ibn Sarjadah.

"Do join us," David ben Zakkai welcomed him hospitably. "Soon we will say the *Minchah,* afternoon prayers, and perhaps after that you will join us in the third Sabbath meal."

Saadia felt that he could not stay on with Ibn Sarjadah, even for a little while. "Rabbi Abraham awaits me," he said, "and will concern himself unnecessarily if I tarry."

"Your Rabbi Abraham watches over you as though you were a babe in swaddling clothes," Ibn Sarjadah jibed.

The Exilarch threw back his head and laughed.

The remark was unkind and uncalled for. It was more like the insult of a jealous child than the remark of a mature and responsible man. Saadia clenched his lips and restrained himself from speaking.

Ibn Sarjadah glanced slyly at Saadia, his eyes narrow

as slits in his fat jowled face. "It does not strike your fancy, my remark?"

Saadia hesitated a moment. It was foolish to take issue over such a trifle. He certainly did not want to become involved in an argumentative discussion, especially before the Exilarch. His truthful nature battled with his common sense.

"I hardly heard what was being said," he answered carelessly, making as though to leave.

"Ah, then," Ibn Sarjadah purred, "my words are not worthy of notice."

The Exilarch, meanwhile, sat up and watched with amusement the parrying between the two men.

"I did not say that. But now that you mention it," Saadia said carefully, "they indeed are not worthy of notice. I find you a vain man, unmindful of the feelings of others. You are too ambitious and greedy, and as a result your honesty is weak and watered. Many times your words do not mean what they say. Why then should anyone take notice of them?"

Ibn Sarjadah's face reddened with anger. "Is this the way of the righteous man, to insult another to his face?"

"It is better than the way of one who insults another or demeans him when his back is turned," Saadia retorted.

Ibn Sarjadah raised himself from his chair. His chins quivered on his chest, but his eyes were firm and hard as steel. "I will always remember your comments on my personality and character, Saadia ben Joseph. Some day you will regret having spoken them."

"If you are threatening——" Saadia started mildly.

"Come, come." David ben Zakkai tugged at Ibn Sarjadah's robes. "Let us forget this nonsense. You know Saadia, Aaron. You should not have spoken lightly of one who is dear to him. Saadia, for his part, is a forthright man, and sometimes says things that would have better remained unsaid. There is a small failing in each of us——"

Saadia interrupted him. "Do not make apologies for me, Ben Zakkai. I have said only what I meant to say—and what should have been said. And now, I bid you both a Good Sabbath."

With that, the Egyptian scholar walked out of the room. Although he never consciously tried to avoid him, Saadia did not meet Ibn Sarjadah face to face again for the rest of his stay in Bagdad. A tragic note from Sara dispelled the incident from his mind completely. Sara wrote that on the very eve of their departure from Fayyum, Saadia's father, Joseph, had died.

"Perhaps it was the excitement of looking forward to the trip, of once again seeing you—we will never know," Sara wrote. "The doctor says that his heart simply gave way. He died peacefully in his sleep. When we came to rouse him in the morning, he was gone. Oh, my husband, I know how this sad news will grieve you, for even my quill weeps as it speeds across the parchment. I beg of you, take comfort in our faith.

Comfort yourself even as you have comforted others. . . . The Lord hath given and the Lord hath taken away."

Saadia wept bitterly. He had so looked forward to kissing his beloved father once again, to spending hours in study with him, to sharing the dreams and plans he held for the future. Now it was gone. All his yearnings and his hopes were shattered.

For seven days Saadia mourned his father in the fashion prescribed by Jewish law. He sat on the floor, his robe torn and his head strewn with ashes. Rabbi Abraham and Mustafa hovered anxiously over him lest he fall ill with melancholia. A steady stream of visitors from the community, offering condolences and comfort, kept Saadia's mind occupied. In the evening he was too exhausted to do anything but fall into a troubled sleep.

As soon as the mourning period was over, Mustafa and Rabbi Abraham began preparations to leave Bagdad for Sura. Because Saadia was still grieving for his father, the community did not think it proper to give him a festive farewell. The elders came with their blessings and good wishes, and with tears in their eyes begged him to remember Bagdad as his second home. "Saadia Alluf," they called him. The pleasure in the new title was almost gone for Saadia.

The new Alluf was thinner, the lines on his face deeper, and the gray in his hair more prominent. He turned to the study of Torah for his comfort, and there his zeal was greater than ever. He prayed each day of the journey, that Sara and his son would arrive safely in Sura.

In 922, just seven years after he had left his beloved wife in the courtyard of the synagogue at Fayyum, Saadia and Sara were reunited in Sura.

The two academies in Babylonia, Sura and Pumbedita, had been steadily declining in influence because of lack of strong and continued leadership. Sura especially suffered, for the Gaonim who were appointed by the Exilarch seemed to have a short life span, and Gaon after Gaon came and went as the head of the academy. Pumbedita seemed to be somewhat more fortunate, and as a result there seemed to be a better and stronger organization in that institution.

At the time that Saadia came to the academy of Sura, the Gaon of Pumbedita was Kohen Zedek, an able and energetic man who attracted many disciples because of his personality. He had been at the head of the academy for quite a few years, and had built it up financially as well as in the fields of scholarship.

At Sura, the Gaon Yom Tov Kahana was a simple and insignificant man. "I was a weaver by trade," he told Saadia, "and why Ben Zakkai appointed me to this important position, I will never know."

Saadia too wondered. Was it because David ben Zakkai did not want to antagonize Kohen Zedek in Pumbedita by placing an equally strong leader in Sura? Knowing Ben Zakkai's character, Saadia felt that the Exilarch would rather play one man off against another. The question remained unanswered in his mind. This was all part of politics, and the very thought of it displeased Saadia. He shook it off.

In the years that followed, Saadia was unbelievably happy. His family was growing, and the sweet sound of his children's voices and Sara's happy face dispelled any moments of gloom that he might have had. His mind was at ease now, and he was free to study, to compile many notes and background material for a great work that was taking root in his mind. It would be his life's work—a philosophic treatise. In this work he would prove that religious belief could exist side by side with scientific knowledge.

As Saadia's correspondence with scholars all over the world grew more and more voluminous, Rabbi Abraham engaged the services of a young student, to sort the questions and help arrange them in systematic order. More and more Jews began to associate Sura with the name of Saadia. He was the only one who took a firm stand on major issues, who encouraged those Jewish communities which were far distant and weakening, who explained Jewish law so that it lived on in every aspect of life. There was no problem too small or too big which Saadia, as Alluf of Sura, could not deal with.

In the year 928, the unassuming Yom Tov Kahana died. A new Gaon would have to be appointed by David ben Zakkai. There was confusion and chaos in

Sura, as many ambitious scholars began to think of themselves in terms of the princely position.

Rabbi Abraham, who never for a moment lost faith in his belief in Saadia as one of the greatest leaders of his day, walked about the house with a secret smile on his lips.

"Just wait and see," he told Sara. "Your beloved husband will be Gaon of the academy of Sura. He will set it on its feet once again, and return it to its past glories."

Sara was embroidering a silken bag for Saadia's tallith, and her busy hands stopped for a moment. "I do not want it for him," she said earnestly, "unless he wants it himself. He has too many responsibilities. He works long into the night. I do not care for titles or honors. I care only for Saadia."

"As do I, dear Sara," Rabbi Abraham answered. "Whatever the Lord wills, so be it." But in his heart of hearts, he hoped and prayed that Saadia would be chosen.

As for Saadia himself, he hardly was aware of all that was taking place. He had written David ben Zakkai a letter urging him to send Judah to Sura, to live with him and study with him. David ben Zakkai's answer had pleased Saadia greatly.

"It will be my pleasure to bring Judah to my dear friend and revered rabbi, so that he may sit at his feet and absorb the Torah. I shall be in Sura directly, and Judah, your son as well as mine, will accompany me.

For is it not written, the teacher of a child is as though he were that child's parent?"

Thus it was that Saadia hardly associated David ben Zakkai's visit to Sura with a new appointment to the Gaonate. He was too busy reacquainting himself with Judah, whom he loved equally with his own children. Judah was to be one of the household now, and Sara was as overjoyed at having him as her own husband was. Anyone whom Saadia loved, Sara loved.

It was a difficult decision that David ben Zakkai had to make. For many years he had been careful of the feelings of Kohen Zedek, the Gaon of Pumbedita. And now Sura had so diminished in prestige that the Exilarch held very little hope for its future. It was a dying cause as far as David ben Zakkai was concerned. For some days now, he had thought of Saadia for this position. This would be merely an honor, nothing more—for Sura really held no prestige. Would Saadia accept the position that really was a position in name only? And then again, what if by some miracle Saadia were able to revitalize the academy, to breathe new life into the withered bones? What then?

In many ways, David ben Zakkai mused, Saadia was a reflection of himself. It was as though he were looking into a mirror. Saadia was strong, courageous, a man who did not bandy words, a man of principle, forthright and honest. Yes, such a man might work miracles in Sura.

But was Saadia ready for the job? Remembering how he talked to Ibn Sarjadah caused the Exilarch to reflect.

Saadia was not a patient man. Nor could you call him a diplomat. He was a man who called a spade a spade.

And there was Kohen Zedek to think about. How would he feel with a strong leader in Sura? David ben Zakkai chuckled. The thought of two men squared off against each other appealed to him more and more.

Finally David ben Zakkai made his decision. He ordered his carriers to take him to the home of Nissi Nahrawani. Crowds gathered in the street to watch his litter go by. As the people bowed, they wondered who the new Gaon would be. Would it be Nissi Nahrawani himself?

Nissi Nahrawani, another Alluf at the academy, was renowned throughout Sura for his great piety and scholarship. Unfortunately a mysterious disease had ravaged his body and left him blind. Afflicted though he was, the blind man remained kind and loving, never questioning the way of the Lord.

He greeted David ben Zakkai warmly, for the two were old friends, and Nissi had often acted as mediator between the Exilarch and Kohen Zedek in their disputes and differences.

"It is a great pleasure to see you in Sura," Nissi said. "I am sure, however, that you are here for more than a trip of pleasure. No doubt you have come to seek a new Gaon."

"I think I have found him," David ben Zakkai answered.

"Good. Good. It does not reflect well when a position remains open for too long a time. I mourn the passing of Rabbi Yom Tov, for we have lost a fine man. A simple man, but one who was motivated only by good and pure thoughts."

David ben Zakkai had hardly come to hear a eulogy of the late Gaon of Sura, but he forced himself to listen politely.

Rabbi Nissi suddenly interrupted himself. "I am most derelict in my duties. I have not offered you anything to drink. Or to eat, perhaps? I have a woman servant who will gladly——"

"No, no." The Exilarch waved it away with his hand. He looked about the sparsely furnished room, the worn and threadbare robe worn by Rabbi Nissi, and made a mental note to send a large basket of food and supplies the very next day.

"Well then?" Rabbi Nissi asked the question and waited patiently, as only the blind can, for the answer.

"I think I have found him," David ben Zakkai repeated.

"And who is it?"

"You."

"Me?" Nissi Nahrawani asked the question mildly, with no trace of surprise in his voice.

The Exilarch leaned forward and took both the hands of the blind scholar in his own. "I have come to appoint you the head of the academy in Sura."

There was not a tremor in the thin, wasted hands, nothing to indicate any inner excitement. "It is a great honor," Nissi said steadily, "which I must refuse. We are not so destitute of scholars that the blind shall serve as leaders."

"You do yourself an injustice, Rabbi Nissi." David ben Zakkai did not relinquish his hold on the other's hands. "There are many who have eyes and see not. You have eyes that see. They see into the very heart of man."

Nissi smiled. "I thank our Lord for all His blessings, but my dear David, the blessing of sight is not mine. You must choose a man for this task who has all his senses about him."

David ben Zakkai sat still, searching the guileless face before him. "It is a great honor," he said.

"It will be an equally great honor for me to serve anyone you choose."

"But you must serve. I need you now. I am in a dilemma——"

"My dear David, I cannot." The words were said with a quietness that was final. The question was closed. With a sigh, the Exilarch leaned back in his chair. He turned the rings on his fingers, catching the light first in this stone, then in the next.

"Who then would you suggest, Rabbi Nissi?" he finally asked.

"I cannot help you, my son. I have never envied men in high places for just this reason. You have such weighty decisions to make, decisions which you alone can make. The responsibility is a grave one. You will have to make the choice yourself."

David ben Zakkai left off playing with his rings, and rose from his chair. He looked out of the window of the blind man's study. In the square two little boys were drawing stick figures in the sand. With thin tree branches, they kept drawing figures of men and erasing them. Drawing and erasing. Drawing and erasing.

David ben Zakkai watched them for a long time while Nissi sat still, waiting patiently.

"I can make a man," the Exilarch broke the silence, his voice exultant. "I can suddenly bring him out in Jewish life and make him as real as the figure the children draw in sand."

Rabbi Nissi shook his head sorrowfully. "Do not delude yourself. You make no man. God alone can make him. The men you think you give substance to are as unreal as the drawings you speak about."

David ben Zakkai hardly heard him. Pounding one fist into the palm of the other, he repeated, "I can make a man. I can give him power and prestige. I can choose someone who is no one, and make him the most important human being in the world."

Rabbi Nissi continued to shake his head. "I pity you, David."

"Why? Why do you say that?"

"I pity any man who thinks so much of his own will. The Lord can put it all to naught. Power passes, man returns to dust from whence he comes. You rejoice only in what is passing, what means nothing in man's lifetime. That is why I pity you."

But the Exilarch was too enthused with his own sense of power to pay attention to the words of the blind Rabbi. With one stride, he was at his side. "Enough of philosophic discussions. Let me ask you. What do you think of Saadia ben Joseph as Gaon of Sura?"

The sudden question brought Rabbi Nissi to his feet, so that the two men stood side by side, facing each other. "You should not ask me," Nissi Nahrawani whispered.

"But I do," David ben Zakkai answered.

"Then I must speak the truth. Saadia is a man of unusual learning and great character. But he is not a man whose picture you can draw and erase at will. You have used the phrase 'to make a man.' Well then, I can tell you now that once you 'make' Saadia, you can never unmake him."

There was a long silence in the shabby room.

"What are you telling me?" David ben Zakkai finally asked.

"My son, do not cause me to speak unnecessarily. Saadia is a man of great wisdom and extraordinary learning, of eloquence and piety. He will not see his new position as one granted by you, but rather as one granted by God. He will not consider anybody's wishes in the world. He will think only in terms of the greater good."

"And that is what we want, isn't it?" the Exilarch asked.

"Yes. That is what we want. But is it what you want?"

David ben Zakkai laughed. He put one arm affectionately around the frail figure. "If it's a clash of wills you are worried about, we will jump that hurdle when we come to it. As for me, you have helped me make my decision. I will definitely appoint Saadia as the new Gaon."

Nissi Nahrawani inclined his head. "Do as you have determined. I shall be the first to sit at Saadia's feet and hearken to his words."

"So be it." The two men parted cordially.

That very night David ben Zakkai wrote to Kohen Zedek informing him of his decision. The reply of the Gaon of Pumbedita was formal and polite. He accepted the announcement with good grace, and extended a formal invitation that Saadia be installed as Gaon of Sura in his own academy in Pumbedita.

As soon as Kohen Zedek's reply came, David ben Zakkai paid a call upon Saadia. Nissi Nahrawani had not said a word about his interview with the Exilarch, and there was no one in Sura who knew that a decision had been reached. The Exilarch pictured in his mind the surprise and astonishment that Saadia would display. He was sure the young Egyptian rabbi would be overjoyed at the appointment.

It was with chagrin that he watched Saadia's face as he offered him the position. The only change that came over it was of regret.

"I will not be able to continue my writing."

"Of course you will. The academy of Sura is nothing much to work at."

"If I accept, I will make it something much."

The words "if I accept" stung the Exilarch. "I must have your answer now," he said curtly.

"Yes," Saadia murmured, "We're back to the fish in the Sea of Galilee. Yes. Your answer, David ben Zakkai is yes."

In the month of Iyyar, in the year 928, Saadia ben Joseph was officially and solemnly installed as Gaon of Sura. And all the way home to Bagdad, David ben Zakkai kept hearing the blind man's warning.

5

Saadia Expelled

A NEW SPIRIT was infused into the academy of Sura. Whereas up until Saadia's installation as Gaon there had been just a tiny trickle of applications for membership, now Rabbi Abraham and his assistant were deluged with requests. Scholars from every part of the world wrote asking for the opportunity to study under the new Gaon.

Saadia was aware that the caliber of the members of the academy would determine its success. For that reason he personally checked all the applications, sorted and resorted them until the best and finest minds were chosen to membership.

Now Sura had to be made financially solvent as well. Up until this time, most of the money donated by the Jewish community had been directed to Kohen Zedek in Pumbedita. Sura was therefore impoverished. It did not even have a fund to subsidize those scholars who lived there. Nissi Nahrawani, the blind scholar, was one of many who received a stipend which was ridiculously small, and caused him to live meagerly. Saadia discussed this matter thoroughly with Kohen Zedek, who reluctantly agreed to give a somewhat larger proportion of the total funds to Sura.

Still, this was not enough. Tirelessly Saadia sent letter after letter to the Jewish communities of the Diaspora, urging them to make a special contribution for the maintenance of Sura. Responses came in gradually. Saadia had keen satisfaction in the large sum of silver sent by the Jews of Aleppo. "For Rabbi Saadia Gaon, he who wrought miracles in Aleppo . . ." their letter read. Saadia smiled. How gullible man was! Miracles indeed!

As more money came in, as great scholars moved to Sura, the academy began to regain its lost prestige. Saadia reinstituted a weekly Shiur, a lecture on the Torah, which attracted Jews from near and far. More and more questions of Jewish law came to be directed toward Sura rather than to Pumbedita. People began to talk of *the* Gaon. They almost forgot about Kohen Zedek, for Saadia's strong personality was beginning to hold the reins of Jewish life tightly in his hands.

One afternoon Nissi Nahrawani asked for permission to have a special audience with Saadia. Rabbi Abraham immediately made room on the Gaon's busy schedule, for Nissi was revered and venerated, and Saadia never liked to keep any of his colleagues waiting, especially one such as Nissi.

Rabbi Abraham ushered Nissi into Saadia's study, unobtrusively helping the blind man to find a chair. Nissi had become thinner and frailer than ever. Saadia pushed back the parchments on his table, and leaned forward.

"Peace unto you, Rabbi Nissi," he said.

"And unto you and yours," the gentle voice replied. "It has been a long time since I have availed myself of the opportunity to sit with you, dear teacher."

Saadia winced. Such was the humility of the ancient scholar sitting before him that he was able to call a man half his age "his teacher"!

"I wish you would come more often," Saadia answered. "You know there are few people with whom I share my burdens. Rabbi Abraham is perhaps the only one. I am not a man who is able to be friends with many. Perhaps I am destined to loneliness. Nevertheless, I must tell you that any visit from you would be a welcome one."

Someone else might have found Saadia's words strange, but Nissi recognized in them a true evaluation and honest self-appraisal.

"I thank you. And I thank you too for the basket of pomegranates which you sent to my home. The meat of the pomegranate is my favorite dish, as you must so well have learned."

Saadia flushed. He could not bear the intimate display of emotion. "It was nothing. Nothing at all." He riffled the parchments on his desk.

Rabbi Nissi's sweet face was calm. "As you know, dear teacher, I have reached the age of threescore and ten, and the years left to me are few indeed. I would like to see my loved ones happy and secure, and it is for that reason that I come to you this afternoon. My brother's daughter is a pious and learned child, who possesses the beauty of the spirit as well as the beauty of the body. She has come of a marriageable age, and I would like to see her married to a learned man, a scholar among our people."

Saadia waited as the old man paused to wipe his brow. Within him he was thinking of how many important affairs he had to deal with. Then of course, he could have been working on his notes. He was angry with himself for being displeased with Rabbi Nissi for taking his time over such a trifle. He tried to show interest, but the older man had been talking for some time, and Saadia had completely missed what was being said.

"I beg your pardon," Saadia interrupted. "I did not hear your words." He leaned toward his visitor.

"I was suggesting that a marriage contract be drawn up between my niece Tamar and your *ben bayit,* the son of your household, Judah."

"My Judah?" Saadia was astonished. Judah had been living with him these last years, and he had hardly realized how the boy had grown to man's estate under his very eyes. Yes, it was an excellent suggestion. The boy should be married. "But you know, of course, Rabbi Nissi, that Judah is the son of David ben Zakkai. You require his consent, not mine, happy though I would be to give it."

"Judah is the son of your spirit, though he is the fruit of David ben Zakkai's loins. May I ask you, then, to write our Exilarch and obtain the necessary permission?"

"It is done." Saadia rose joyfully, glad that the interview was of so short a duration. He led the old scholar to the door. "May this be the beginning of many happy events for all of us. It will be a wonderful alliance—the house of Nahrawani with the house of Ben Zakkai. Rabbi Abraham," he called out, "help our dear friend cross the courtyard to his litter."

"There is no need to trouble yourself," Rabbi Nissi protested. "I have this stick——"

"Let me be your stick this once," Rabbi Abraham said. "It will be an honor for me to serve you."

"Peace, peace," Rabbi Nissi said in farewell, waving away Rabbi Abraham's implied compliment, but leaning upon him nevertheless.

"Peace and good fortune for all," Saadia answered heartily. He could not wait to get back to his desk and write to the Exilarch. A wonderful idea had struck him in the last few moments of Rabbi Nissi's visit. He had been wondering how to write Ben Zakkai in the matter of the disputed inheritance that had come before him. Now he knew. He would combine the good news with the bad. Hearing about Judah's possible marriage would soften the blow in the other matter. David ben Zakkai would be too busy thinking of his son to concern himself with a trifling legal document. In this fashion it might all be smoothed over.

Saadia sat down and began to compose the letter.

"May this find my friend David ben Zakkai and all his family in the best of health. I write to ask the permission and consent of the Exilarch to give the hand of his son, Judah, in marriage to Tamar, the niece of Nissi Nahrawani. I am sure I need not describe the virtues of the bride, for she comes of a distinguished and learned family. I have not mentioned the amount of her dowry, but these are matters that can be arranged after I receive your consent.

"In the matter of the dispute over the inheritance which you forwarded to me for my signature, I regret that I have not yet signed the Document of Settlement. I cannot condone the need to give one-tenth the disputed amount to the Exilarch. This money belongs to the parties involved." Saadia paused. He could see David ben Zakkai's face, the veins in his neck swollen with purple rage. Was there any way to soften the blow? Raising his quill, he began to write once again.

"However, since you need Kohen Zedek's signature as well as mine, I have forwarded the Document to Pumbedita. Perhaps you and I can in the meanwhile discuss this further."

He sanded the parchment, sealed it, and asked one of his lads to send it off by early messenger.

It was a messy business. Two people fighting like cats over the money was distasteful enough. But it was outright dishonest for the Exilarch to take one-tenth of the amount for himself, even before a decision had been made. It was against all the principles of Jewish law. The fact that this was customary practice did not make it right, Saadia reasoned. It was best to stop it now. He had no intention of ever signing the document. If Kohen Zedek read his arguments through carefully, Saadia was sure he too would not sign. If David ben Zakkai was a judge of men, and Saadia was sure he was, then he might as well forget not only about this one dispute but about the whole custom of getting money from litigants.

It was with dismay that he read two letters which, ironically enough, arrived on the same day a week later. One was from Kohen Zedek, returning the Document of Settlement, signed with his own signature. Saadia was stunned. He had been sure that Kohen Zedek would uphold him in this stand. Kohen Zedek had not even troubled himself to acknowledge Saadia's letter with its lengthy explanation.

The other letter was from David ben Zakkai, professing joy at the forthcoming marriage of his son, pooh-poohing any thought of a dowry, for he could give the young couple all they needed. It was the last paragraph which disturbed Saadia.

"What is this nonsense of refusing to sign my Document of Settlement? This is a mere legal formality which requires no thought on your part. I am sure that by now you have already affixed your signature.

"I shall ask you to set the wedding of my son before the Passover holiday, when I can arrange to be in Sura. I look forward to seeing you then."

Carefully Saadia placed the Exilarch's letter on top of the legal document which Kohen Zedek had already signed. He would forget about it for now. It was too bad that the Exilarch did not realize that he would never sign it.

Judah received the news of his forthcoming marriage with great happiness. He had heard of Tamar's gentle spirit and great beauty, and he was glad that such a bride had been chosen for him. The days until the wedding seemed to stretch endlessly. How he wished winter were over and spring were here! Spring was the herald of Passover, and only a week before Passover, his wedding would take place!

But Rabbi Abraham had a different concern on his mind. He had received a letter from a friend in Bagdad which described a strange twist of events. Ibn Sarjadah, the man whom Saadia disliked so intensely, was now David ben Zakkai's favorite, present with him at all state occasions and acting as his chief adviser. He was even traveling to Sura with him!

Rabbi Abraham tried to comfort himself. What if Saadia disliked the Bagdad merchant, and had openly stated so? This should not cause Ibn Sarjadah to act in a vindictive manner. Saadia, for example, would be scrupulously fair, a thousand times more so, when someone whom he did not like was involved!

Rabbi Abraham sighed. If they would only allow Saadia to fulfill his duties as Gaon without these petty distractions. He tried to minimize his fears.

But the arrival of David ben Zakkai with his large retinue including the fat, oily-faced Ibn Sarjadah, aroused them again.

"The Exilarch does not stay at our home this time?" he asked Saadia anxiously.

Saadia was dressing in the simple robe of Gaon, made of blue satin on white velvet, in preparation for a visit to David ben Zakkai. He did not detect the note of anxiety in Abraham's voice.

"Not this time," he answered. "He has come with a great company of servants and other—other——" The face of Ibn Sarjadah rose before him. "And others," Saadia finished lamely. "Now bring Judah here, for I have advised him that it is only fitting that he stay with his father as long as he is in Sura. I am taking him there now, and I hope that at the same time it will give me a free moment with Ben Zakkai. I have an important matter to explain. It must be that he does not understand the reasons for my stand."

"Surely you will not discuss—that is, I do not dare to advise you, Saadia, but in this litigation——"

"I discuss whatever is troubling me whenever I feel

is the right time," Saadia answered sharply. "The Exilarch must have no doubts as to my intentions about that document."

Abraham was still. "Very well. Be it as it will. I will bring Judah to you."

When Saadia and Judah arrived at the inn which Ben Zakkai had completely taken over for himself and for his retinue, he was slightly dismayed to find that his audience with Ben Zakkai was not to be a private one. Ibn Sarjadah was sitting as close to the Exilarch as possible.

"You know Ibn Sarjadah?" David ben Zakkai asked the Gaon.

Saadia inclined his head towards the merchant, half in greeting, half in acknowledgment of the Exilarch's question.

"I must compliment you on the wedding arrangements," David ben Zakkai continued, hardly noticing the wall that existed between the two other men. "I have seen the courtyard of the academy, and Mustafa has certainly outdone himself in bringing so many tables and benches. Let us hope we will have fair weather so that all will go well."

"It will be a most beautiful occasion," Saadia answered cordially, "marking the union of two prominent and learned families. May it bring joy and pride to all Israel."

Judah sat with his eyes downcast, a slight blush on his cheek. It was not fitting for him to participate in the conversation, although he would have loved to prolong it further.

David ben Zakkai pulled a bunch of grapes from the platter before him, ostentatiously pronounced the blessing while everyone watched him closely.

"And the Document of Settlement?" he asked, popping a grape into his mouth. "Did you bring it with you?"

Saadia searched David ben Zakkai's face. There was bland innocence written on it. Next to him, Ibn Sarjadah was smirking openly, while Judah looked confused.

"I brought it. Yes," Saadia replied calmly. "But this is a matter to be discussed between you and me alone."

"If you are referring to Ibn Sarjadah, he is now my chief adviser. He can hear all that has to be heard. As for my son, whether he remains in the room or not is up to you."

Fire sparked in Saadia's eyes. "I keep no secrets, David ben Zakkai. As you so very well must know by now, the Document does not have my signature on it. Nor will it ever be affixed, unless you remove the clause which gives you ten per cent of the estate. This clause must be eliminated from all your Documents of Settlement!"

Ibn Sarjadah leaned forward to whisper something into the Exilarch's ear, something which caused David ben Zakkai to stop eating his grapes. In a note of dismissal, he said, "We will stop this discussion now, and let the matter rest until after the wedding." He rose and turned his back on Saadia.

The Gaon was infuriated by the humiliation shown him. He too rose, opened his mouth as though to say something, and then thought better of it. He turned on his heel and walked out.

Judah ran after him. "Beloved teacher, what is it between my father and you?"

Saadia embraced the young man affectionately. Judah was an *Ilui*—a man of great learning, but he knew little of the outside world. He knew whole passages of the Talmud by memory, but he had very little understanding of the politics of Jewish life. Some day Judah would become aware of this as well. For now, Saadia did not want to burden him needlessly. "It is nothing that concerns you," he said. "It is part of the headache that comes with high office. Did not our sages say, 'He who has been chosen for leadership has been chosen for stones and arrows as well'? It will all pass. It will pass."

The marriage of Judah, the son of David ben Zakkai, to Tamar, the daughter of Avram Nahrawani, took place on the third day of the week, in the month of Nissan, in the courtyard of the Sura academy. A new bridal canopy had been sewed and embroidered by the women of Sura especially in honor of this event. Both the Exilarch and his son were resplendent in magnificent robes and jewels. Next to the simple scholars' gowns worn by Saadia and the Nahrawani family, they looked kingly and overpoweringly wealthy.

It was late evening of a bright, clear day. In the dim light it seemed to Saadia that David ben Zakkai's jewels outshone the pure whiteness of the bride's silk dress. He noted that the Exilarch had even donned his huge badge of office, as if to impress his own importance upon the happy occasion.

At the marriage feast David ben Zakkai found the opportunity to approach Saadia.

"Let us drink a toast together wishing the young couple a long and happy life. You and I have been partners in raising this young man. It is as though we both were his father."

"He has been very dear to me," Saadia answered warmly, pleased by the Exilarch's affability. "May the Lord grant him good years of peace and study. Judah has a keen mind, and he will bring much joy to our people, David ben Zakkai."

"I am pleased to hear it." However, it was not the toast or Judah's learning that was on the Exilarch's mind. "You left the papers with me," he now said casually. "I shall send them in a few days' time to your house for your signature."

Saadia stiffened. "I told you I would not sign them."

David ben Zakkai's tone was still friendly. "Do not be rash, Saadia. The papers will be in your hands immediately after the Sabbath. Sign them, and let us be through with this whole weary affair."

"The Torah does not allow me to sign them just for the sake of 'being through'! It is against principle and law for you to extract ten per cent of the estate for yourself, every time there is a dispute over an inheritance."

"Be that as it may. There are ways to get around the Torah, to circumvent the law. I leave those ways to you. And after the Sabbath you will have the papers."

Saadia shrugged his shoulders. There was nothing to be said.

He was chagrined, however, when, after Sabbath, Judah himself brought the offending papers. The young man's face was aglow, his eyes shining with his own personal happiness when he visited Saadia in his study. Saadia could not be offended by him, seeing his joy. Besides, Judah hardly knew the significance of the Document. Saadia had never discussed it with him.

After they had chatted for a while, Judah brought the papers out from his tunic. "My father sent me with these for you to sign," he said.

"Please tell your father for me that the subject is closed. I cannot sign his papers, for they violate an important religious principle. He must remove the clause which offends me. Then I will be more than glad to affix my signature."

Judah had heard the discussion in his own house between Ibn Sarjadah and his father, and suddenly the pieces fell together. He realized that there was more than a principle of Torah involved. After all, the Exilarch's office had drawn up this Document many years before. It was common practice, and while Saadia was right in wanting to correct it, Judah realized that this was a tug of war between two strong personalities, a war encouraged and fanned by Ibn Sarjadah.

"Can you not close your eyes this once? My father has set his heart on it," the young man faltered, for he did not want to reveal the extent of Ibn Sarjadah's influence on his father, the constant evil talk against Saadia which went on in the household. "I beg of you. Sign the Document. There will be another time to point out the defects in the legal structure."

"He who waits for another time loses all opportunity. I cannot wait. I must deal honestly and fairly each time, as I see it. Go now, and peace be with you."

Dejected, Judah left the house. He tried to soften Saadia's answer when he brought it to David ben Zakkai. But Ibn Sarjadah was there to twist his words into hateful meaning.

"He is pitting his will against yours," Ibn Sarjadah sneered. "Religious principles—bah! He wants to show you he is stronger. Just because Sura has acquired a few thousand silver coins, he has let the power go to his head."

"His will against mine!" David ben Zakkai repeated the words. "I am as strong as he, and stronger!" He shouted as he turned to Judah. "You will go to him with this accursed Document every single day, until we break his will and he signs them!"

"But Father, he never——"

"Every single day, if it takes a month of days! And I

shall wait. I shall wait until he comes begging to me. We will see whose will is stronger, whose will can hold out longer."

There were tears in Judah's eyes. "Desist from this, my Father. It is a trifling sum of money that is involved. Let this not cause a break in the friendship between you and the great Gaon."

"The great Gaon!" Ibn Sarjadah caught the words. "People should be talking rather of the great Exilarch, as they did in the days before this Saadia ben Joseph."

"Ibn Sarjadah is right." David ben Zakkai pulled on his beard. "Saadia is usurping powers that do not belong to him. I have run our legal business in one fashion all these years, following the pattern set by the Exilarchs before me, and I will not allow him to change it. We will hound him every day. Every single day. This will be your task, Judah."

Judah was taken aback. "I cannot. Do not ask it of me."

"What!" Ben Zakkai was astonished. "Are you denying me my request? Are you turning against your own father? Has this man Saadia filled you with such hatred of me that you would even break the fifth commandment? I do not *ask* it of you, Judah. I demand it of you. What is your answer now?"

There was nothing Judah could do. The laws of filial obedience were among the holiest laws of the Torah. He could not refuse his father. He stood there, silent and shamefaced until Ibn Sarjadah pronounced with great satisfaction: "He will do it."

Every afternoon thereafter Judah made his appearance before Saadia. Though David ben Zakkai often gave him special instructions that included terrible threats, Judah turned all these words into friendly pleadings. On the tenth day, the Exilarch delivered a long harangue to Judah, even calling Saadia an abusive name. When Judah made his appearance before the Gaon, the name still quivered before him.

Rabbi Abraham was with Saadia on that day, and he looked at Judah imploringly. "The Gaon is weary. His health is suffering," he whispered.

The whole affair had taken its toll of Judah as well. Always of a delicate physical nature, he now was suffering intermittent pains in the chest. He frequently woke at night, drenched in sweat as a result of these chest pains. He understood what Saadia too must be going through. But he could not respond to Rabbi Abraham's plea. With white face he approached Saadia. The look of annoyance that came over the Gaon's face dismayed him. That he had lived to see the day when Saadia would be annoyed with him, with Judah!

"I plead with you on bended knee, dear teacher. Sign this Document, and let us be free of it. Free to study, to enjoy each other's company once again."

A sorry mood was upon Saadia. Melancholy all day, despondent over the entire affair, he could no longer control his temper.

"How dare you come to me again with your whining and sniveling? Is it gold for your father's coffers that you seek above honesty and decency? Your father dares to breach Jewish law, and you add insult by asking me to sign a dishonest Document?" With a swooping movement, Saadia lifted some silver pieces which were lying on his desk. He threw them in Judah's general direction. "Is this then all that you and your father seek?"

All the pent-up emotions and hardships of the past ten days welled up in Judah. As the silver was flung at him, the overwrought scholar rushed forward and raised his hand as though to strike Saadia.

Rabbi Abraham shouted for help, rushing forward to restrain the trembling Judah. "Mustafa! Help! Mustafa!"

Aghast, Saadia stared at the hand raised against him, at Judah's pale lips and uncomprehending eyes. "What have they done to you, my son? Oh, what evil the Lord has wrought," he whispered, the breath almost gone from his body. "That I should live to see this day!"

The tears began to stream from Judah's eyes, and he hardly felt Mustafa's and Rabbi Abraham's hands as they held him tightly. He wanted to speak, to beg forgiveness, but his tongue was paralyzed and numb, overcome with the enormity of what had occurred.

"Do not come to see me again," Saadia said, the words coming through his lips with an effort. "Never. Never to see me again." His own vision was blurred. This was the young man whom he had trained so patiently, for whom he held such high hopes, whom he loved so dearly. That this, his son, should raise a hand against him! Blood pounded in his ears. He would never be able to forget this wretched moment.

"Go." Rabbi Abraham half pushed, half led Judah. "Go quickly. The Gaon is ill. You must go."

Judah stumbled through the doorway. His body was racked with sobs. He could see Saadia's stricken face swim before his eyes. He never knew how he arrived home that evening. All he remembered was his father asking him a hundred questions while his heart beat violently, and sweat poured over his body.

"What happened? What did he say? Did he harm you? Did he dare lift his hand against you?"

At the last question, a shudder swept Judah's body. He could only weep in reply. "I lost my greatest friend," he sobbed. "I will never be able to go there again. Never."

There was something in the way Judah spoke that made David ben Zakkai realize that he was telling the truth. For one moment he regretted not having followed Saadia's advice to omit the offending clause. After all was said and done, the money meant very little to him. He had so much. And if it was contrary to the spirit of the Torah, of Jewish law . . . He remembered Nissi Nahrawani's warning before he had chosen Saadia as Gaon. Had he not preferred the Egyptian Jew as a man of backbone and strong will, in spite of the blind man's warning? Well, the Gaon was showing his strength now, and he, David ben Zakkai, would defer to it.

But unfortunately, when he returned to his own chambers, Ibn Sarjadah was waiting for him. As the Exilarch recited all that Judah had said, describing his wrought-up appearance, Ibn Sarjadah's face grew hard and cold. His chins quivered as he spoke.

"And will you allow this? Will you allow your son, a descendant of the House of David, to be insulted by a man to whom you yourself gave position and honor? Will you allow the prestige of the Exilarch to be lowered in the eyes of the people? This refusal to sign an unimportant Document is just a ruse, a means of testing your strength. Once you submit to Saadia, you will be submitting forever after."

David ben Zakkai saw flames dart before his eyes. He had never looked at it in that fashion. How dare Saadia insult his son! What right did he have? He smote the table with his hands. "But what can I do?" he asked, more of himself than of Ibn Sarjadah.

The merchant pursued his advantage. "Remove him from office," he answered.

The Exilarch drew back, his face ashen. "It is a terrible thing, a terrible thing to do."

"Are you afraid, then?" Ibn Sarjadah taunted. "You who always boast of the fact that you can make men and break them. Are you really afraid to break an arrogant, wilful man like Saadia, the son of some low-born Joseph?"

Shrewdly, the merchant had pointed out how Saadia came of common stock, and how David ben Zakkai was far above him. But the Exilarch had hardly heard him. In his mind's eye he saw two little boys playing in the sand, drawing figures and erasing them, drawing and erasing. He could hear Nissi Nahrawani's voice, laughing at him. He would show them all. He would show them that David ben Zakkai was no toy to trifle with.

"Bring me parchment and quill," he said in a choked voice to Ibn Sarjadah.

"Then you will do it!" Ibn Sarjadah's voice held a note of triumph.

"I will write to Kohen Zedek in Pumbedita. It is he who must write the excommunication of Saadia. He and I together will sign the decree declaring Saadia out of the Jewish fold."

Ibn Sarjadah turned to hide his gloating pleasure. "You will have no trouble with Kohen Zedek." He hesitated a moment. "And the position of Gaon?" he asked slowly.

"It will be open now. I do not care who gets it. You can appoint anyone you wish."

Ibn Sarjadah sighed in relief. Now Saadia would see that Aaron ibn Sarjadah was not a man to be made light of.

Saadia's first feeling when the decree of excommunication reached him was one of overpowering grief. The pain he felt that the friendship between the Exilarch and himself had to end so tragically was almost unbearable. In anguish he searched his soul for the divine reason for all that had occurred. Certainly he had been right in refusing to sign a dishonest Document. Was this, then, what Jewish scholarship was doomed to? To be used at the whim of any man's personal desires?

Saadia locked himself up in his study and would not

allow anyone to enter. He would not even turn to his holy books, or to his writings, for comfort. All he could see before him was Judah's hand raised against him. Judah . . . Judah . . . Sometimes a vision of the Exilarch's haughty manner as he remembered it at Judah's wedding came before him. Sometimes it was Ibn Sarjadah's cunning face. But most of the time it was Judah. The pain of losing Judah overwhelmed all other pain.

Locked in his study day after day, he thought and thought. Was all that he had done for the Jewish people so little? His fight against the Karaites which united the Jews more strongly than ever; his struggle against his colleague Ben Meir and the efforts to change the calendar; his labor on behalf of the academy of Sura, to help restore it to its former glory; the hundreds of letters he had written; people he had advised. Was all this worth so little that David ben Zakkai could perform one shameful act against him and wipe it all away?

For three days and three nights Saadia pondered, refusing food or water. Thoughts and visions pressed on his brain. One afternoon he fell into a stupor, half asleep. Suddenly his old friend of the peaceful days in Tiberias appeared before him. Abu Kathir's eyes had aged, but his face was the same open, friendly face that Saadia remembered so well.

"Do not become so despairing, Saadia *b'nee*. There is justice in the world. And there is a divine reason for all that happens. You have never feared to start afresh—not when you left Egypt or Tiberias or Aleppo. You can start afresh now. And you will return in triumph to Sura. Mark my words well."

"Then am I to accept this—this——" Saadia stumbled as he spoke the words aloud to his dream-vision.

The vision of Abu Kathir smiled at him. "Accept? No. Fight? Yes. Bring the issue to the people, to the

Caliph himself if necessary. He who fights on the side of righteousness is always rewarded."

Saadia's head was spinning. "The people . . . the Caliph." He repeated the words to impress them upon his memory. "But all my life I have fought to keep my people united. Shall I now be the instrument to divide them?"

"Out of divisiveness will come greater strength," Abu Kathir reassured him.

"Then I must. . . . There is no choice but to fight David ben Zakkai. . . . Once again I am a fish in the Sea of Galilee."

Abu Kathir did not seem surprised at Saadia's last sentence. He smiled lovingly. Saadia tried to say more, but the vision had disappeared. There was only the dim light of the study. But it was enough. Abu Kathir had shown him the way.

Weak and dazed, Saadia staggered to the door. He was so ill with fasting that he could hardly remove the bolt. Finally the door was open. The anxious faces of Rabbi Abraham, Sara and Mustafa swam up at him.

"Master, you never answered when we knocked," Mustafa breathed.

"Water. . . ." Saadia muttered.

Mustafa ran to the pitcher and filled a drinking bowl with water. The Gaon drank thirstily.

Sara wrung her hands at the sight of her drawn, emaciated husband. "Oh, my lord, my husband, you did your body a grievous sin by refusing food and water these many days." She tried to touch him timidly, and was both relieved and happy that Saadia drew her near and leaned upon her.

"It has not hurt me. It has shown me the way. Abu Kathir showed me the way——"

The words "Abu Kathir" were scarcely out of his mouth when he felt Sara's body shudder beneath his weight, at the same time that a strange glance passed between Rabbi Abraham and Mustafa.

"What is it?" Saadia asked. "What is wrong?"

"Abu Kathir," Abraham answered. "You mentioned Abu Kathir. But he—but he—I beg of you, Saadia, do not look so stricken. He was a man gone in years. The good Lord saw fit to take him from us. It was while you —that is, we heard the news while you—while you—"

Saadia's knees buckled so that Abraham ran to help Sara support him. "Blessed is the Judge of Righteousness," he said, repeating the words one always pronounced when one heard of a death. But he could not believe it. "My good friend with whom I just spoke . . . Abu Kathir gone." Hunger and weakness together with the shocking news made him faint. As he lost consciousness, he heard himself say clearly and distinctly:

"I will fight. I will let the people know. I will bring it to the Caliph!"

6

In the Court of the Caliph

ALTHOUGH the delivery of correspondence between Jewish communities often took weeks, the news of Saadia's excommunication spread rapidly. For many people, the news was as shocking as it was frightening.

"What did the great Gaon do to deserve this?" men asked each other.

In cities where Saadia's personality had been felt, in cities such as Aleppo, Tiberias, Bagdad and Fayyum, giant rallies were held, and proclamations were read, declaring that the Exilarch David ben Zakkai had exceeded his limits by interfering with the Gaon. In other cities, delegations of Jews were appointed to travel to Sura to meet with Saadia and to bring back a report as to the general state of affairs.

It was a time of great confusion, for although David ben Zakkai had appointed a new Gaon, Saadia would not leave Sura or his position. He remained at the academy, continuing his usual routine, lecturing to his students, writing, and meeting with representatives from all over the world. A curt note from the Exilarch reminded him that he was no longer Gaon, and that someone else had been appointed in his place. Saadia coolly responded that he for his part was now appointing a new Exilarch to take David ben Zakkai's place. This was his way of answering that the Exilarch no longer held his respect or his obedience.

Months went by in this fashion—Saadia unyielding, the Exilarch fuming, and the people disturbed and bewildered. Judgments that Saadia handed down were reversed by the Exilarch, so that a man who was awarded ten pieces of silver in a damage suit would suddenly find that his opponent was awarded twice as much by the Exilarch.

It was a tragic affair. Saadia's soul was distressed that he had taken the fight to the people, and that they were the ones who were being hurt most. They were torn, divided by loyalties and frightened by malicious gossip and rumors. Ibn Sarjadah and his henchmen were doing a good job of spreading all sorts of wild slander, even including Sara and Saadia's children in their filthy rumors. This above all grieved the great Gaon—that his people whom he had united in belief and tradition were once again subjected to doubts and confusion.

And now it was as in the days of Fayyum. Mustafa

took to guarding his master day and night. It was no unusual occurrence for friends or supporters of Saadia to be cruelly and mercilessly beaten by blackguards hired for the job. The life of the Gaon was in great danger, and many urged him to leave Sura until all the furor had subsided and died down.

But Saadia remembered Abu Kathir's words in the vision he had had of him: "There is still justice. . . . There is a divine reason for all the pain and suffering." His fight against the Karaites in Egypt had led to his wandering until it had made him Alluf and the Gaon of Sura. His fight against the Exilarch, too, would lead him to fulfill God's will. Stubbornly and patiently he waited.

Caliph Al-Muktadir, who was governing the vast Mohammedan Empire, enjoyed a reputation for fairness and honesty. Saadia was reluctant to bring the argument between the Exilarch and himself before someone outside the Jewish people. But he saw that there was too much at stake. He must not allow himself to become an instrument for the division of his beloved people. Unless something was done soon the damage would be irreparable. He therefore pondered and searched the innermost recesses of his soul, until he finally decided to write to the Caliph. His note was brief.

"To the Right Royal Caliph Al-Muktadir, descendant of the prophet Mohammed and Just Ruler over all the Dominions of the East:

"May this missive find His Greatness in the best of health. There is a matter of grave disagreement between the servants of the Caliph, David ben Zakkai, Exilarch of the Jewish community, and Saadia ben Joseph, Gaon of Sura. It would please the undersigned if the Caliph were to judge between the two parties concerned. The undersigned would be happy to abide by the judgment of the Caliph, whose justice and righteousness are known throughout his kingdom.

"I await the favor of a reply from His Royal Highness, and am at his disposal, as ever."

Saadia placed his own seal upon the letter, and sent it off to Bagdad by private messenger. At the same time, he thought it only right to inform David ben Zakkai of his intentions. Rather than write the Exilarch himself, he instructed Rabbi Abraham to see that the information reached his former friend.

Former friend! The words were bitter on his tongue. Studying with his baby son Dosa, one night, Saadia recalled those wonderful hours when David ben Zakkai's Judah had been as a son to him. He had not seen Judah since the day the young man dared to raise a hand against him. Nevertheless, Nissi Nahrawani kept him informed as to his health and happiness. Saddia knew that Judah and Tamar were expecting the birth of their first child, and that the young man had become thinner and paler, and did not look at all well. That very day Nissi had mentioned that Judah seemed to be fading away. The blind man had turned his face to Saadia with such a look of pleading that the Gaon, in order to cover his own inner turmoil and distress, had been moved to make an abrupt and cruel response.

"Whatever happens to Judah, it is not my affair," he had said.

The words stung him now. His own Sara was expecting a child—their fifth—and Saadia looked at her lovingly. She was hovering over him as usual, her high cheek bones flushed with pleasure that he was spending time with his family. Dosa's child-voice intoned the language of the Gemorrah, but Saadia hardly heard him. Did Sara see Tamar, he wondered? His love for Judah welled up in him, and he spoke his thoughts.

"Sara, it would be well if you were to visit with Tamar," he said aloud. "What has happened between ——" He could not mention the name, lest he would show his emotions and cry. Again he started. "What has happened between her husband and me should not affect your friendship."

Sara averted her eyes. "My husband, I am glad you speak of this matter. I have been deceiving you these many months, and it caused me sleepless nights. I must confess to you now that I have indeed been visiting with Tamar. Judah is ailing, with a terrible chest pain which leaves him weak and dizzy. And she, poor girl, is troubled and fearful. I hope I did not offend you, my lord?"

Offend? Saadia's heart leaped with gladness that Sara was helping his once beloved adopted son. "You did not offend me," Saadia answered his wife. "You pleased me as always." He paused. He wanted to ask more particulars concerning Judah's health. Pains in the chest sounded ominous. His wide reading of the sciences told him it might very well be a weakening of the heart. Pray God that it was not so! The short and cruel answer he had given Nissi that very afternoon plagued him more than ever. "Whatever happens to Judah," he half said to himself, "it *is* my affair."

Sara caught the words. "O, my lord, I am so glad that you do not bear him any malice."

"Malice?" Saadia looked up in surprise. "He who bears malice against his fellow man, forcing it on his relatives and dear ones, bears malice against himself."

No, he did not bear Judah any malice. Nor could he ever. He caressed Dosa's hand fondly. Judah himself was as dear to him as his own little Dosa. How could he bear his own child malice?

Sara decided to speak her mind. "My husband," she began, "since you have written to the Caliph for a trial between Ben Zakkai and yourself, you have become another man—more at ease, calmer."

"It is because the decision is out of my hands," Saadia readily replied. "What will be God's will, will be. I cannot allow this terrible situation to continue. Now that I have taken the step, I can only be patient and wait."

"Could you not, now, see fit to visit Judah, so that it might once again be as it was between you?"

"I? Visit Judah? After he tried to assault me? After he lifted his hand against me? Should not he, rather, come to see me?"

The very fact that Saadia was continuing the subject made Sara bolder. Her next words came in a rush. "He pines for you, Saadia—but he fears to approach you.

He has often spoken with Rabbi Abraham about an audience with you. Rabbi Abraham advised him against it. He is sick, Saadia, sick with the need of you. Tamar tells me that he does not sleep nights, remembering the day when——"

"I cannot forget it myself," Saadia said, biting his lips. "I cannot blot it out of my memory."

"O Saadia, my husband, perform this great deed of kindness. A word from you, and Judah would be healed. I know it."

"Will his father allow him?" Saadia asked musingly.

"He is a man for himself. He has broken all ties with Ben Zakkai. There are those who say he even spat at Ibn Sarjadah. I cannot picture my gentle Judah doing any such thing. But that is neither here nor there. Saadia, will you send a message to him? Some token that will show him that you are ready to receive him once again?"

In his heart of hearts, Saadia was delighted that Sara had opened the way for him to see Judah again. "You are in the right, my wife. I will ask Rabbi Abraham to see him for me. Truth to tell, I am most anxious . . ." The words hung in mid-air.

So it was that a few days later, a trembling Judah stood before Saadia. The Gaon noted with apprehension how thin and pale Judah looked.

"I welcome you with both my arms," Saadia said, rushing toward Judah to embrace him.

"I must ask your forgiveness," Judah said. "These months have been torturous for me. I never meant to

—it was the great and awful pressure—I never would have——"

"What has been, has been," Saadia interrupted. "Let us speak only of the future."

But Judah could not stop. "I lost both my fathers at one time. My soul could not bear it. It has also made my body weaker."

"You will be strong once again," Saadia encouraged him. The older man spoke on in a soft, comforting voice until Judah felt at ease, and the warmth between them was as in olden times. They were closeted together for more than an hour, and finally, reluctantly, Judah rose to go.

"What is between my father and you will never concern us again," he said earnestly to Saadia. "I beg of you that our friendship may continue uninterrupted."

Saadia was reminded of the pending trial at the Caliph's court. He felt it only right to mention the fact to Judah, but the younger man would not allow him to continue.

"I do not even wish to hear of it," he affirmed passionately. "Whatever will be, will be."

The court of the Caliph Al-Muktadir was a rich and splendid one. Saadia had heard of the magnificent palace the Caliph had built for himself, but it was not until he was called to the Judgment Room that he became aware of the lavish beauty about him. Hand-woven tapestries of intricate design and gorgeous colors hung on the walls. The trim on the woodwork was solid gold, as were the hanging light fixtures. A pure marble floor was covered with a rug so thick and rich that Saadia felt as though he were sinking into it with every step. The stained glass windows with their multicolored prisms bathed the whole room in a warm and glowing light, and the gold everywhere glittered and shone.

Saadia and Rabbi Abraham entered the room when it was already half filled with petitioners. Both Ben Zakkai and Ibn Sarjadah were already present. Ibn Sarjadah seemed to have grown fatter and sleeker, if such a thing was possible. But David ben Zakkai looked like a shadow of his former self. Although he was clothed in his royal and majestic robes, and the turban on his head glittered with the semiprecious jewels of his office, his face was ashen. He did not avert his eyes from Saadia's face, nor did he seem to see him. It was as though his mind was in some far distant place.

Saadia strode forward purposefully. In this first meeting with the Exilarch, he was determined to be cordial. "Peace unto you," he said, trying to include Ibn Sarjadah in his greeting, although it galled him to do so. "May the Caliph's judgment today bring an end to strife and discord among the leadership of the people of Israel."

David ben Zakkai shook himself as though he were being roused from a dream. "So be it," he muttered.

"Will you then accept the Caliph's judgment even if it be against you?" Ibn Sarjadah asked sneeringly.

"I have come here for just that reason," Saadia answered simply and with great dignity. "He who bears no respect for the judge can never hope to hear justice."

Ibn Sarjadah laughed. "We will hear justice today. You need not concern yourself on that score." He poked the Exilarch in the ribs. "Won't we, Ben Zakkai?"

The Exilarch looked confused, and did not answer.

Holding his head erect, Saadia walked off. "David ben Zakkai is a man whose spirit is broken," he commented to Rabbi Abraham.

"They say it is a bewitchment by that devil, Ibn Sarjadah. He is an Exilarch in name only, for Aaron ibn Sarjadah issues the orders and speaks in his name."

"There is something that worries me about Sarjadah's attitude. He has something planned, something underhanded. . . ."

"Not with Al-Muktadir," Abraham reassured Saadia. "The Caliph has ordered many men to prison simply because they tried to bribe him."

"Still . . ." Saadia's doubts remained. Ibn Sarjadah had been too confident.

The Judgment Room had meanwhile been quietly filling up. Rich Arabs in gaudy headdresses, poor Bedouins in their cotton kaffiyehs—all came to be judged by their ruler, the Caliph. Mustafa had been mingling with the crowd, listening to snatches of conversation here and there. Suddenly he appeared at Saadia's elbow. He pulled both Saadia and Rabbi Abraham aside.

"There is great danger lurking. It is an evil day for Allah," he whispered.

"What did you hear?" Rabbi Abraham asked.

"There have been the usual rumors of an uprising

against the Caliph. But the army officer who craves his position is in the room now. I do not like the way he and his henchmen talk. What if there were to be an assassination at this very hour? Great rabbi, I sense it in my bones. We would do well to leave this entire trial for another time."

"Nonsense," Saadia answered.

"This must be the usual court intrigue," Rabbi Abraham said, his voice betraying his nervousness. But he tried to look assured. "Everything seems calm here. Besides, all this hardly concerns the Gaon."

"I hope not," Mustafa answered. "In any case, the army officer is here now. He is called Al-Kahir, and he stands in the far corner, in the center of that group of ruffians. You would do well to keep half an eye on him, and move close to the door as soon as possible."

Rabbi Abraham trembled. "Perhaps it would be best if we——"

A look from Saadia cut him short.

Fearfully, Abraham turned to stare at Al-Kahir. He was a short, swarthy Arab with bushy eyebrows and a long, pointed nose. He seemed to be in a state of great happiness, for his even white teeth shone in a perpetual smile.

"He looks evil," Rabbi Abraham said to Saadia.

"He who judges at a glance shall in turn be judged at a glance," Saadia reprimanded him.

"Nevertheless," Abraham mumbled half to himself, "the evil of his soul shines forth."

A sudden commotion at the doors, followed simultaneously by three majestic sounding clashes of the cymbals, heralded the Caliph's arrival. He wore a long, flowing robe over his tunic and silk trousers. Although he was an old man, the face under the turban was calm and unlined. His shrewd eyes appraised the large gathering as he walked up to the throne. They rested a fraction of a moment longer than necessary on Al-Kahir, and a twisted smile crossed the Caliph's lips. Mustafa had pulled Saadia and Abraham to the floor in a bow of homage as the Caliph passed them. But not before Saadia could look into the Caliph's eyes. The look he saw there puzzled him. "I have seen that look in men who are about to die," Saadia thought to himself. Could Mustafa's premonition be right? Was an assassination to take place in that very room? And did the Caliph know about it?

The noise of the cymbals died away, and the Caliph's voice was heard in blessing and welcome. As soon as the ruler was seated, the Minister of Justice stepped forward.

"We have before us a plea for judgment between the Gaon, Saadia ben Joseph and the Exilarch, David ben Zakkai," he announced.

Ibn Sarjadah darted to the throne. "Your Royal Highness, in this matter between——"

The Caliph motioned to him to stop talking. In slow, unhurried speech, he addressed himself to the merchant, his eyes, however, staring blankly into space.

"The litigation has been instituted by the Rabbi Saadia ben Joseph, and not by yourself, Aaron ibn Sarjadah. It is more fitting and proper, then, that he who complains speaks first. I will therefore call upon Saadia ben Joseph to state the case, and if you are representing the defendant, David ben Zakkai, I will then give you due time to answer the charges."

Ibn Sarjadah tried to disguise his rage. He had surely thought that since he knew the Caliph so well, any trial in which he was associated would be dealt with to his advantage. He saw now that the reputation held by the Caliph as a man of justice was indeed true. Why, he might even rule in favor of Saadia! Ibn Sarjadah stroked his beard. It was a good thing this other matter was coming up—for the Caliph's judgment wouldn't matter much in any case. The silver he had slipped into Al-Kahir's eager palm . . . Had David ben Zakkai realized what was happening? Did he know what was going to happen? Perhaps even today, in this Judgment Room . . . The merchant looked out from under his brows at David ben Zakkai. The latter looked desperately ill. He hardly paid attention to what was going on. It's just as well, Ibn Sarjadah thought.

Saadia, for his part, thought nothing of the Caliph's comment. It sounded just, and he accepted it at its face value. Not knowing the protocol of the court, he stood by and waited. The Caliph's Minister of Justice finally called his name.

"If the Rabbi Saadia ben Joseph is present in the Judgment Room, he is asked to step forward."

With great dignity, Saadia stood before the Caliph. His hair and beard were almost completely white, but his carriage was straight and erect.

"You are Saadia ben Joseph, Gaon of Sura?" the Minister asked of him.

"I am he."

"State your case briefly."

In a few sentences, Saadia explained what had transpired, how he had been excommunicated and relieved of his position because of a moral and religious obligation. "I could not sign a document which was against the principles not only of my faith, but of decency and honesty. The Exilarch had no right to take unto himself any part of the money in question. It did not belong to him. I ask you now, Your Royal Highness, to pass judgment as to whether or not I am to be retained as Gaon of Sura or to be excommunicated from my office."

The Caliph had listened intently. When Saadia concluded, he leaned forward.

"Is it not your duty as Gaon to decide on all moral, religious and ethical questions which face your people?"

"It is."

"And is it not the duty of my good friend the Exilarch, David ben Zakkai, to act as the representative of the Jews among the nations of the world—in the political, social and economic areas?"

"It is."

"Well then, it seems to me that David ben Zakkai must accept guidance from you on religious issues, just as you must accept guidance from him on political issues."

Ibn Sarjadah stepped forward. "If it please Your Highness——"

"How do you enter this picture?" the Caliph Al-Muktadir smiled at him. "I know that you are a businessman, but I see you now as a man of words and legal knowledge. Are you, then, acting for the plaintiff in the case?"

"If it please Your Highness, I am indeed acting for David ben Zakkai whose physical illness this wretch, Saadia ben Joseph, has taken advantage of."

Saadia interrupted indignantly. It was the first time in his life he had heard himself called a name. But he refrained from commenting on it. "I did not know the Exilarch was ill," he said.

"You lie!" Ibn Sarjadah ejaculated. "You waited these many weeks, hoping the illness would be fatal, and that there would be no need for this trial. Else why did you delay so long in coming to our Caliph?"

Saadia was taken aback. He could not lower himself to this man's depths. How smoothly, how cunningly Ibn Sarjadah had distracted the Caliph from the important aspects of the case! And why was David ben Zakkai so silent, standing there as if he were in a trance? Was it true that he was really so ill?

"I will not stoop to name-calling," Saadia said in a voice quivering with emotion. "Rather will I ask His Highness, the Caliph, to judge between the Exilarch and myself on the merits of the case placed before him."

The Caliph Al-Muktadir had been watching all three men closely. "I have read the brief sent to me by Ibn Sarjadah and I have heard the complainant, Saadia ben Joseph. There is only one judgment to pass—that which is for the right. It would seem to me that Saadia ben Joseph exercised his prerogative as Gaon in correcting a practice which David ben Zakkai was following. It would also seem to me that David ben Zakkai, in refusing to recognize the Gaon's domain, is at fault. However——" The Caliph had seen Ibn Sarjadah step forward, and he now raised a hand asking for attention. "However, I will try my utmost to be fair to both sides. I will therefore study the case overnight. You will hear my judgment in the morning."

Saadia inclined his head in acceptance, and walked back to Rabbi Abraham. Ibn Sarjadah had already pulled the Minister of Justice to one side, and was talking volubly to him.

What happened in the next few moments was like a nightmare. There seemed to be a pressing of bodies about the chair of the Caliph; one horrifying, inhuman shriek was heard, and suddenly Al-Kahir, the Arab revolutionary was standing on the Caliph's chair—the old ruler lying dead at his feet.

Al-Kahir lifted a bloody knife. "This will be the judgment from now on!" he shouted. "We have planned this day well. The Caliph's men are my men, and the Caliph's throne is my throne. If there are any here who stand for Al-Muktadir, let them speak up now." He laughed at his own joke. "No, there is no one here for

Muktadir. Now, therefore let us curse his name, curse the dead dog who lies here at my feet—and bless the name of Al-Kahir, the new Caliph of Bagdad!"

The crowd prostrated itself. Saadia and Rabbi Abraham glanced around them in terror. Mustafa, ever resourceful, pushed them down on the floor, almost lying on top of them.

The rabble-rouser's voice went on, promising the Arabs great wonders under his reign. Saadia felt the blood pound in his face. To think that this knave was now to be ruler over so many thousands of people! It was a frightening thought that a man who had neither moderation nor justice, learning or knowledge, was now in a position to make decisions for an entire multitude.

"Your case is lost," Mustafa whispered. "Master, this man can be bought by the highest bidder. If you give me silver, perhaps I can outbid Ibn Sarjadah."

"Watch your lips, Mustafa," Rabbi Abraham, trembling though he was, rebuked the servant. "How dare you think your master would stoop to bribery?"

"I said it jestingly, Rabbi Abraham. I meant only to show that our business with the Caliph is done. We can hope for no justice from that one."

The new Caliph, meanwhile, had finished his peroration, and surrounded by his bodyguards, stalked from the room.

Pale and spent, Saadia rose. The Arabs were talking excitedly in a babble of voices. The dead Caliph lay at the foot of the throne, the rug beneath him darkened by his blood. All this Saadia saw as in a dream. This was his first encounter with calculated bloodshed and violence, and he felt ill. He was sick at heart at man's cruelty to his fellow man, at his greed and avarice. Bewildered, he stood there.

David ben Zakkai was gone. He must have left the room immediately, Saadia thought. But Ibn Sarjadah was still present, his eyes narrow as they calmly watched Saadia.

"We had better be off," Rabbi Abraham urged. "This is not a time or a place for Jews. One never knows when the wrath and the tempest spills over onto any of the unfortunates who are around."

"I would never have believed it," Saadia muttered to himself. "To see murder committed, and not a hand lifted in protest, not a voice raised in outrage!"

"Hmph!" Mustafa snorted, deftly pulling and pushing Saadia to the door. "The hand that would be lifted would be cut off, and the voice that would be raised would be stilled forever. All bow to the one in power."

Outside of the palace, the streets of Bagdad were deserted. The shutters were closed, but Saadia felt as though the people of Islam were watchfully waiting to see the turn of events. The inn where Mustafa had arranged lodgings for the two rabbis was as still as death. Even the innkeeper was not in sight.

"You see," Mustafa voiced their thoughts for them as they climbed wearily to their quarters, "evil news travels fast. The people fear for their lives. Doors are bolted and shut against the Angel of Death."

It had been a long, hard day. Saadia lay on his mattress, too spent to think. After a while he fell into a fitful sleep, disturbed by visions of Al-Muktadir, David ben Zakkai and the Angel of Death.

The first decrees issued by the new Caliph Al-Kahir reversed all decisions made by his predecessor. Murderers and thieves were released from prison. For a small amount of silver, any decision could be bought from Al-Kahir. Nevertheless, Saadia stubbornly held onto his faith.

"He has all the information. He heard Al-Muktadir practically own that we were in the right. We will wait for his decision. It must be in our favor."

The hours of waiting stretched into days. Saadia passed the time in his usual fashion, writing and studying and receiving visitors. One of the latter turned out to be the father-in-law of Ibn Sarjadah, a man by the name of Bishr, whom Saadia knew only slightly. The audience with Bishr started out in a strained and unfriendly fashion, for Saadia could not disguise his feelings for Ibn Sarjadah. But Bishr had come on a special mission.

"I represent the entire Jewish community of Bagdad," he said, his simple face and candid eyes reflecting his inner honesty. "I am sorely distressed by what has happened between my son-in-law, Aaron ibn Sarjadah, and yourself. I can only say, would the good Lord that it were not so! But it is for the community of Bagdad that I have come to speak—and not for myself alone.

For them, for all of us, I beg of you, Saadia, do not leave the Gaonate. Remain with us in Bagdad and be our master, making this your office."

"I can do nothing until I hear the judgment of the Caliph."

"Pah!" Bishr exclaimed. "Al-Kahir can be bought by anyone. Why abide by a judgment that is bought with silver? Stay with us in Bagdad, forget the entire trial, and remain Gaon of your people."

"As for staying in Bagdad, that I cannot decide now. But happy as I am to hear your kind words, Bishr, I must answer that the question of the position of the Gaonate is out of my hands," Saadia replied. "I have told all concerned that I will abide by the decision of the Caliph, and abide I will. I have already resigned myself to the fact that in all likelihood——" The great leader could not finish the sentence. Instead, he rose in an abrupt gesture. "Bishr, Bishr—I wish I could tell you how ill this has made me. I am sick at heart for all the men of the world who solve their problems by bloodshed and fighting. I am sick for kings and kingdoms that fall at the hands of knaves and rascals. I am sick for David ben Zakkai who is no longer a tower of strength, but is now a body without a soul. Yes, I am even sick for your son-in-law, Aaron ibn Sarjadah, who knows only the crooked and deceitful way of life. And lastly, I am sick for myself, whose hands are to be tied so that they no longer can write and work for my people."

Bishr now rose too. "Great Gaon, your hands are tied only if you wish them to be tied. And now I can no longer pretend. I came with news in my heart, but I could not speak it. I half hoped you would ignore it, and it was for that reason that I urged you to keep the office of Gaon. The Caliph Al-Kahir has decreed that you are to be banished from Sura, removed from the position of Gaon. I hold the document in my tunic."

Saadia turned slowly. "So," he sighed. "So."

"I myself chose to be the bearer of these ill tidings," Bishr continued falteringly. "Since I feel myself partly responsible because the evil came from my son-in-law. But you know that the judgment is false, that it was bought and paid for——"

Saadia waved to him to stop speaking. "So," he said. "It is all for naught. The years of wandering . . . the years of hard labor . . . the dreams."

Bishr remained silent.

"Where shall I go?" Saadia murmured. "Where have I not been? Egypt? Palestine? Syria?"

"I plead with you," Bishr interrupted. "We, your people, need you. Do not think of any other place to go, but stay here in Bagdad. It would be a great honor to us if you would do so. Great rabbi, I need not tell you, with your great wisdom and faith, that the Divine Hand has written these events for a purpose. It is for you to find that purpose now."

"Yes—a purpose. I must find the divine purpose." Saadia seemed stunned by the news of his banishment, and was standing transfixed.

Bishr motioned helplessly with his hands. He wondered what to say, and finding no words, placed the document of banishment on the table. "A worthless document," he said emotionally, "written by a worthless hand." He half turned to go, then prompted by love and great affection for the man who had dedicated his life to Judaism, he fell on the floor at Saadia's feet and kissed the hem of his garment. "Great rabbi, do not

despair. I, as well as every other Jew of Bagdad, am at your disposal."

"I do not despair," Saadia said slowly. "As long as the Holy One, blessed be He, breathes life into my soul, I will not despair. Go now, Bishr, my friend, and God be with you."

Alone, Saadia read and reread the Document of

Banishment. He read it detachedly, as though it concerned someone else, but not Saadia ben Joseph.

"He who is banished will return in triumph," he said to himself. "A purpose. Abu Kathir told it to me in my vision of him, and Bishr repeated it again today. God's purpose in all this is what I must find."

PART THREE

Victory and Peace

7

Reconciliation

RABBI ABRAHAM took the announcement of Saadia's banishment much harder than his beloved rabbi. A fever grasped hold of his brain, and he was in great danger of dying. Both Saadia and Mustafa waited on him day and night, cooling his brow with wet compresses and forcing liquids between his parched lips. Rabbi Abraham's illness caused Saadia to forget for a while the great disaster which had befallen him. He saw no visitors, did not even open his correspondence. He was completely out of touch with the outside world.

This was the first time in Jewish history that a Gaon, a great leader and rabbi, had been deposed from his position. It was a sad and a tragic note, but Saadia did not allow his mind to dwell on it. Instead, he began perusing his notes, the notes on Jewish philosophy and thought that he had made all these years. He would not allow himself to dwell on what had happened. Instead, he was going to think of the future.

In the weeks that Rabbi Abraham lay feverish and incoherent on his bed, raving about Ibn Sarjadah and the wrong that had been done to Saadia, Saadia himself rewrote old lectures and developed new ideas. He worked close to where Rabbi Abraham lay, so that he could always be of help. Poor Rabbi Abraham! He hardly recognized anyone, even staring vacantly into the face of his beloved Saadia.

The doctors had advised that Abraham be sponged frequently, to cool the fever of his body, and this Mustafa and Saadia took turns doing. They had almost lost hope that Abraham would be himself once again when one day, thanks to the Lord, Rabbi Abraham opened his eyes, and they were clear.

"Saadia, my rabbi," he said weakly. "What has happened to me?"

Saadia was overjoyed to see that his friend was rational once again. The fever had left his brain!

"You were ill, my beloved friend," he answered rising from the manuscript he was studying, and taking Abraham's thin wasted hand between his own. "But the fever has left your body. You have since been asleep, a quiet, restful sleep, and now you will get well."

"Are we still in Bagdad?"

"Yes," Saadia smiled. "It has been three weeks since you became ill, and we are still in Bagdad."

"Then the year is the same?"

Saadia paused for a moment. The question seemed so strange. "Yes, yes. It is still the same year 932."

"Ahhhhh," Rabbi Abraham sighed. "I had hoped it wasn't . . . that the clock had turned back . . . that you were not banished . . . that we were still in Sura. . . ."

Saadia leaned closer to the sick man, smoothing his brow affectionately. "Why do you worry yourself so, my friend? I have found the divine purpose in this banishment from the Gaonate—and I am happy. I have even sent for Sara and the children to join us here in Bagdad."

"Happy? Here—in Bagdad?"

"Yes, here. Look, I have finally been given the opportunity to finish my life's work." Saadia held the parchment he had been studying close to Rabbi Abraham's face. "It is not every man who is relieved of all responsibility and can devote himself to his writing. But this great privilege has been granted to me. Remember how we were searching for a name for the manuscript? Well, I finally found it. I will call it Emunot V'Deot—Faith and Knowledge. I have tried to incorporate all that science and our religion have to say about the universe." Animated and excited, Saadia went on, outlining his entire book.

An amazed look passed over Rabbi Abraham's face. "This banishment does not dismay you then?"

"Banishment?" Saadia looked as though he had never heard of the word. "Who can banish a man who has faith in his heart? There is no caliph in the world who can banish me from my God."

Abraham smiled peacefully. "O, master. I worried so, lest you become ill as when . . . with Judah . . ."

A shadow crossed Saadia's face. He had heard disquieting news from Sura regarding Judah's health. The young man was failing rapidly. Saadia could not step foot into Sura to visit him—and Judah could not leave because of his poor health. It grieved Saadia greatly, for he had heard that Judah was blaming himself for Saadia's banishment.

"Do not fret over me," Saadia said warmly to Rabbi Abraham, trying to calm his own fears as well. "Rather fret over yourself. I need you now more than ever, and you must get well."

The old man closed his eyes contentedly. "I will. I will."

As Rabbi Abraham became stronger, Saadia took to reading excerpts to him, writing and rewriting difficult sections of the book. He lost track of time, immersed as he was in his new work, and it was only when Sara arrived that he realized that months of correspondence had piled up.

Since Rabbi Abraham was still too weak to handle his affairs, Sara efficiently arranged for two young rabbinical students to come in each morning and to sort the requests that needed responses from those that didn't.

It was with great amazement that they found that almost all of the letters had silver enclosed, begging

Saadia to accept each gift as a token of the great esteem in which they held him. The letters came from all four corners of the earth. The community of Aleppo had sent a hundred talents of silver, and the governor a warm letter pleading with Saadia to spend the rest of his days in that community.

Every letter expressed horror and contempt for the intrigues of Aaron ibn Sarjadah. The people hailed Saadia as the Gaon, regardless of who was now appointed to take his place in Sura. They would never recognize anyone else as their leader.

Saadia was moved and stirred at the reverence and affection shown him. He had surely thought that he would be forgotten by now. He began to devote a part of his day to the correspondence, answering the many requests that deluged his office. Rabbi Abraham, after a month of recuperation, was well enough to assume his former responsibilities. Once again the day assumed a familiar pattern. In the mornings Saadia would work on Faith and Knowledge. In the afternoons he would write Responsa and receive visitors.

After a year or two had gone by in this fashion, it became accepted for the entire world Jewish community to recognize Saadia as their spiritual leader. Once again they came to him with their litigations, their problems and their troubles. The puppet Gaon whom David ben Zakkai had appointed in Sura was totally disregarded. Instead, Jews from all over the world preferred to make the long trek to Bagdad, bringing with them their problems and disputes.

About four years after Saadia's banishment, it happened that a Jew from Aleppo came into argument with a Bagdad Jew over some property which they both held jointly. The Jew from Aleppo, having heard of Saadia as the miracle-working rabbi, insisted on taking the litigation to Saadia to settle. The Bagdad Jew favored David ben Zakkai. So each went to his own judge.

Aaron ibn Sarjadah, annoyed more than ever at the open manner in which Saadia was hailed leader, decided to use this opportunity to teach the Jewish community a lesson. Late one night, when the Jew from Aleppo was returning to his inn, Aaron ibn Sarjadah and some hired blackguards waylaid the defenseless Jew and beat him unconscious.

The news of this incident outraged all of Bagdad. Bishr, the head of the Jewish community, once and for all cut all ties with his son-in-law, Aaron ibn Sarjadah. Taking the poor, bruised Aleppo Jew with him, Bishr stormed into David ben Zakkai's house.

"This is where your pride and your arrogance have led you!" he shouted at the Exilarch. "To be led by the nose by such as Aaron ibn Sarjadah—does this fit a descendant of the House of David? See what he has done—he has even used force to help you win. He stops at nothing. He stoops to violence and bloodshed, to deception and bribery. How long will your eyes be closed, David ben Zakkai? How long?"

The Exilarch turned a sorrowful face towards Bishr. "Do not berate me now, Bishr. Heap ashes on my head;

tear my clothes. Help me grieve for my great loss, my great, irreplaceable loss!"

Bishr's mouth hung open. He saw now that the Exilarch's eyes were red with weeping, that his hair and beard were dishevelled. "What is it? What has happened?"

"My sins have returned to visit me," David ben Zakkai wept. "Judah—my beloved Judah——"

"Have you heard from Sura, then?" Bishr asked, still not comprehending fully what his eyes and ears told him.

"I have heard. A messenger has brought me the last letter ever written by Judah, my son. He is gone now, gone to his eternal rest! What a blind fool I have been, Bishr! What a blind, stupid fool! Now that I have lost the jewel in my crown, now that those days I might have spent with my son are gone forever—now I see it all. Leave me to mourn, Bishr—for I cannot speak further lest my heart break in a million fragments, as his, poor boy, did. Leave me to mourn the untimely death of my son. When the seven days are over, we shall do what has to be done."

"Blessed is the Judge of Righteousness," Bishr pronounced, having heard the confirmation of Judah's death. The news upset him. He had heard of the young man from Saadia. The Gaon often said that Judah was a genius, a great mind which would some day be a pride to the Jewish people. And now the great genius was dead.

Bishr could say no more. He and the Jew from Aleppo hastened out of the house, back to Bishr's own quarters where irate Jews were still milling about.

"How long will the Exilarch keep up his quarrel with our Gaon without fearing God's punishment?" One of these Jews called out when Bishr entered.

"He has been punished already," Bishr answered. "Judah, his son, has passed into the eternal world."

A hush fell on the crowd.

"An omen from the Almighty," someone whispered fearfully.

"A sad omen," Bishr repeated. "But I think that it will bring to an end the quarrel between David ben Zakkai and Saadia ben Joseph. When the Exilarch's seven days of mourning are over I will visit with him at length. He will agree to a reconciliation—of that I am almost certain."

"Pray God that it be so," one ancient said. "We have had enough strife in our midst."

"Judah dead?" another interrupted. "It will break Saadia's heart. He speaks incessantly of the boy, and I know he writes him long letters daily."

"His heart has been broken enough these last years," another chimed in. "He has had only sorrow and troubles."

Bishr let the crowd talk on, commiserating with the Gaon and feeling his pain. He had sent his servants to bring Rabbi Abraham to him, to ask his advice on how to break the news to Saadia.

But alas! The bad news had traveled on lightning

wings. The same messenger from Sura had stopped at Saadia's house as well. Both Sara and Saadia had collapsed with grief at the news of the tragic death. Although they knew how ill Judah had been these last years, they were hopeful that his failing heart would hold out a little longer. Saadia's house was a house of mourning. It was as though he had lost his own son. He read once again every one of Judah's letters of the last years, conjuring up the dear face, the faithful eyes. Some days he could not believe it, and he would speak irrationally of traveling to Sura despite the banishment to see Judah for himself. Other days he would sit morosely, staring into space, not even Dosa's hug helping his melancholy.

As soon as seven days of mourning were over, Bishr once again went to visit David ben Zakkai. It was a great shock for him to see Aaron ibn Sarjadah there as well. Was the relationship between them still the same?

But David ben Zakkai, haggard and drawn-looking though he was, had recaptured some of the spark of his early days. Ibn Sarjadah was sitting there, his face a greenish yellow.

"Do not fret, Bishr," David ben Zakkai said. "I have had a great deal to say to your son-in-law, and I chose the first opportunity to say it. I have been speaking very frankly. I am sure it has pained Ibn Sarjadah as much as it has pained me. He has agreed that we have let our own greed and ambition lead us into wrong paths and evil ways these last years. Is that not so, Aaron?"

Ibn Sarjadah attempted a sickly smile.

So! It was the old David ben Zakkai once again, holding the reins, conscious of good and evil. Bishr was delighted. It would make his task here relatively easy.

"Will you then make peace with Saadia?" Bishr asked of the Exilarch. "Abandon whatever animosity there was between you. Let all be peace once again."

David ben Zakkai bit his lower lip, saying nothing. At this, Aaron ibn Sarjadah leaned forward eagerly. "You certainly will not—" he began.

"Silence!" David ben Zakkai shouted, his eyes flashing. "How dare you tell me what I certainly will or will not do! I have had enough of you, Aaron ibn Sarjadah. I do not know what reasons motivated you—but you came between me and my son, between me and the best friend I ever had."

Ibn Sarjadah rose stiffly. "There is no need for me here."

"I did not dismiss you," the Exilarch answered, with a glint in his eye.

Aaron ibn Sarjadah hesitated. To spurn the authority of the Exilarch and to leave would mean a break with him forever. He swallowed his pride and sat down.

"What say you?" Bishr asked, more hopeful than ever. "Will you see Saadia and resume your old friendship once again?"

David ben Zakkai turned his gaunt face towards Bishr. "My son Judah requested it of me in his last letter," he said.

"Then you will do it?"

"I will do it."

Overjoyed, Bishr almost kissed the Exilarch. "Tomorrow," he said, wishing it could be this very moment. "Tomorrow. I will arrange for a meeting between you at that time."

"But tomorrow is the Fast of Esther," the Exilarch halfheartedly objected.

"Then do me the great honor of breaking the fast at my home," Bishr said. "I will invite Saadia as well, and for the Jews of the world today there will be light and joy and gladness, just as there was for the Jews of Shushan."

The Exilarch nodded his head in assent. "Very well. May it be as you say."

Saadia, when he was approached by Bishr an hour or two later, was more than happy to make peace. Although he had found a measure of tranquility these last years, finishing his life work, he knew that his greatest service was to be in daily contact with his people. They needed his advice and his guidance. True, his home in Bagdad was a center of Jewish learning, but it was not the same as the academy at Sura.

Another strong factor was Saadia's determination to help Tamar raise Judah's child. The boy was still a tot, and Saadia had vowed to himself, as soon as the news of Judah's death had reached him, that he would raise the little boy as he had raised Judah. In this Sara wholeheartedly agreed.

When Bishr, then, came to Saadia with the announcement that the Exilarch would be happy to meet in reconciliation, Saadia readily agreed.

"Strife and disharmony tear at a man's heart. I am glad to see an end to all the friction. Besides, David ben Zakkai was once my friend. The sparks remain, and need only the warm breath of friendship to rekindle them." Then Saadia raised the same question that the Exilarch had raised. "But why tomorrow? It is the Fast of Esther. I would not——"

"No, no," Bishr interrupted. "It is my honor and great privilege to ask you and the Exilarch to break the fast at my home. We can recite the evening prayers and listen to the reading of the Scroll of Esther together. We will form our own *minyan*. There will be no difficulty whatsoever in obtaining the ten men necessary for communal prayer. So many want to come, the difficulty lies in keeping them out."

"In that case," Saadia responded, unable to hide the happiness he felt, "in that case, I will be there."

By late afternoon of the next day, a great crowd had assembled both at the home of David ben Zakkai and that of Saadia ben Joseph. They were eager to witness the historic meeting between the two great men.

The Exilarch had dressed himself in his magnificent robes of office, and as he left his home, going on foot and refusing the services of a litter, hundreds of Jews followed him. Saadia, for his part, had not deviated from his usual scholar's robe. He was followed by a reverential mass of people, shouting his name and blessing his virtues.

The two processions slowly approached Bishr's house.

David ben Zakkai, when he first caught sight of

Saadia, blanched, and the tears filled his eyes. He stopped in his path, and the mass of Jews behind him, misunderstanding his halting, shoved him on.

"Onward, great Exilarch!" they shouted at him encouragingly. "Do not stop now."

Saadia saw the halting steps of his former friend. He realized that it was a difficult thing for the proud and haughty Exilarch to be doing. Stretching his hands towards him, Saadia called his name.

"David ben Zakkai, blessed be your name. I bid you peace from the depths of my heart."

Now the Exilarch was weeping openly. Thankfully, he rushed toward Saadia, embracing him warmly.

"My rabbi," David ben Zakkai said, a possessive term which he had never before used. "I beg your forgiveness for all that has transpired."

"My great friend," Saadia said. "We both erred. I beg you to forgive me my stubbornness."

Disregarding the many people who were craning to get a closer view of the reconciliation, the Exilarch and the Gaon entered Bishr's house arm in arm. Bishr, grateful to the Lord that he had been instrumental in bringing the two great men together, bubbled over with excitement.

"Soon, soon." He ran from one guest to another. "It will be time for *Mincha,* the afternoon services. Then we will be ready to usher in the Purim holiday. And, after that, we will feast in honor of this great occasion."

Saadia and David ben Zakkai hardly heard him. They were engrossed in their conversation, and Judah's name was frequently pronounced. After six years of bitterness and fighting, there was only warmth and friendship between the two men. They were both great enough not to harbor any grudge. Each secretly admired and respected the other. The rancor of the last years was gone.

"We cannot stay here, on public view, as it were," David ben Zakkai said impulsively. "Do come to my home for the Feast of Purim. We will enjoy the Purim meal together, without the benefit of these gawking people."

Saadia looked questioningly at Rabbi Abraham.

"I know that Sara and the students will wait up for the Gaon and for his disciples," Rabbi Abraham hesitated.

"Good." David ben Zakkai was once again his old, authoritative self. "We'll arrange to have them all transported to my home."

When Rabbi Abraham demurred again, Saadia interrupted. "Let it be as the Exilarch wishes. We will bring the children and the students to David ben Zakkai's home."

"At such short notice? How will we do it?"

"Is that scalawag Mustafa still with you?" David ben Zakkai asked. When he received an affirmative reply, he continued. "That's your answer. You leave it to Mustafa. There is nothing that that man cannot accomplish, if he so wishes."

So it was that Purim was spent at the home of David ben Zakkai. While the disciples of Saadia feasted and rejoiced in the traditional manner, the two men spent long hours catching up with each other. They spoke until the small hours of the morning, parting reluctantly for a nap. Saadia sent for his manuscript Faith and Knowledge, and the reading of it so enthused the Exilarch that he ordered scribes to recopy it at his own expense, so that it might be distributed throughout the Jewish world.

"You have used these years for self-fulfillment," David ben Zakkai said to Saadia. "I, instead, have burned out the holy spark that was within me. I am naught but a shell."

"Do not say it," Saadia interrupted. "We all have times of failure and times of success. You will rise once again to the heights you held in the past."

David ben Zakkai shook his head regretfully. "I am too old. The years left to me are too few."

"Only God knows the years of man. It is not fitting for you to speak in this manner."

"No, my rabbi. Ever since Judah's death, I have felt death within my own bowels. I have not the desire for long life—I am ready whenever the Almighty wishes to take me. There is only one request that I have of you—that you raise Judah's boy as you once raised Judah. Prepare him for the position of Exilarch, for I have no other sons besides Judah, my treasure. Once I am gone, the position will belong to Judah's heir. You know that."

"Do not speak in this fashion," Saadia answered. "Man must never despair or lose hope. However, if it pleases you to hear it, know that I had every intention of taking Judah's and Tamar's son into my home. Your request is as I myself wished it to be."

David ben Zakkai embraced him warmly. "Would that my eyes had been opened sooner," he said.

Sadly enough, although David ben Zakkai held a premonition of his early death, Saadia, with his great faith, never realized that there were only a few years left to his life as well. He and his family moved back to Sura, where the academy reached the greatness it once had held. But a scant four years later, David ben Zakkai died. With his passing a change came over Saadia. Although he tried to eat regularly, and although Sara and Mustafa watched over him lovingly, his body began to lose weight. He became thin as a twig. Occasionally he complained of a pain in his back, but the physicians who were called in could not diagnose the illness. With the loss of weight, Saadia became weaker and weaker. He could not do half the amount of reading and studying he was accustomed to in the past. Nevertheless the Gemorrah manuscript never left his bedside.

The great scholar began to devote more and more of his time to Judah's little boy and to his own son, Dosa. Dosa was proving himself to be almost as great a Talmudic genius as his father, and it was into these two children that Saadia poured all his knowledge, his love of Torah and of Judaism.

Day and night Saadia studied with the two young boys. With superhuman strength, overcoming the weakness of his body, he kept them busy for more than eight hours a day. Abraham and Sara let him be. They recognized the oneness of purpose he was showing.

"He is racing against time," Rabbi Abraham told Sara. Abraham himself, old and weak, was keeping body and soul together only by the Lord's great miracle. "He is racing against time," Abraham repeated sadly.

It was indeed a race against time. Each day found the Gaon weaker. Bones protruded through his skin. His mysterious ailment had left him looking like a skeleton.

Two years after David ben Zakkai's death, on the first day of the week, the 26th of Iyar in the year 942, on the

very anniversary of his installation as Gaon of Sura, Saadia's illness went into its last stages. Although he had not moved from his bed for many months, on this morning he had miraculously been able to rise, to dress himself in prayer shawl and phylacteries, preparing for his morning prayers.

Sara watched him anxiously. "Is it well with you, my master?" she asked.

"Well, well," he whispered hoarsely. "Just remember Dosa . . . Judah's little one. . . . They will carry the torch . . . the fight . . . the fight for . . . unity . . . for our people."

The words left him spent and exhausted. He fell on his mattress.

"Saadia!" Sara cried out. "Do not leave me!"

But the great Gaon had gone where he no longer could hear. A smile of great peace was on his lips. In Dosa and in Judah's son he had assured himself of continuity, of survival. He died contented.

Covenant Books

Stories of Jewish Men and Women To Inspire and Instruct Young People

1. SILVERSMITH OF OLD NEW YORK: MYER MYERS *by William Wise*
2. BORDER HAWK: AUGUST BONDI *by Lloyd Alexander*
3. THE WORLD OF JO DAVIDSON *by Lois Harris Kuhn*
4. JUBAL AND THE PROPHET *by Frieda Clark Hyman*
5. THE UNCOMMON SOLDIER: THE STORY OF MAJOR ALFRED MORDECAI *by Robert D. Abrahams*
6. LIBERTY'S DAUGHTER: THE STORY OF EMMA LAZARUS *by Eve Merriam*
7. KEYS TO A MAGIC DOOR: ISAAC LEIB PERETZ *by Sylvia Rothchild*
8. ABOAB: THE FIRST RABBI OF THE AMERICAS *by Emily Hahn*
9. NORTHWEST PIONEER: THE STORY OF LOUIS FLEISCHNER *by Alfred Apsler*
10. ALBERT EINSTEIN: CITIZEN OF THE WORLD *by William Wise*
11. BUILDERS OF JERUSALEM: IN THE TIME OF NEHEMIAH *by Frieda Clark Hyman*

12 THE FLAGSHIP HOPE: AARON LOPEZ *by Lloyd Alexander*

13 THE SCHOLAR-FIGHTER: THE STORY OF SAADIA GAON *by Libby M. Klaperman*